MW01009515

The route to your roots

When they look back at their formative years, many Indians nostalgically recall the vital part Amar Chitra Katha picture books have played in their lives. It was **ACK – Amar Chitra Katha** – that first gave them a glimpse of their glorious heritage.

Since they were introduced in 1967, there are now **over 400 Amar Chitra Katha** titles to choose from. **Over 90 million copies** have been sold worldwide.

Now the Amar Chitra Katha titles are even more widely available in **1000+ bookstores all across India**. Log on to www.ack-media.com to locate a bookstore near you. If you do not have access to a bookstore, you can buy all the titles through our online store **www.amarchitrakatha.com**. We provide quick delivery anywhere in the world.

To make it easy for you to locate the titles of your choice from our treasure trove of titles, the books are now arranged in five categories.

Epics and Mythology
Best known stories from the Epics and the Puranas

Indian Classics
Enchanting tales from Indian literature

Fables and Humour
Evergreen folktales, legends and tales of wisdom and humour

Bravehearts
Stirring tales of brave men and women of India

Visionaries
Inspiring tales of thinkers, social reformers and nation builders

Amar Chitra Katha Pvt Ltd

© Amar Chitra Katha Pvt Ltd, 2003, Reprinted March 2012, ISBN 978-81-8482-216-8
Published & Printed by Amar Chitra Katha Pvt. Ltd., The Forum, 3rd Floor,
Raghuvanshi Mill Compound, S.B.Marg, Lower Parel (W), Mumbai- 400 013. India
For Consumer Complaints Contact Tel : +91- 22 40497436
Email: customerservice@ack-media.com

The route to your roots

SHAKUNTALA

When King Dushanta frist saw Shakuntala, He was struck by her incomparable beauty and gentle character. He made her his wife and vowed to take her back to his palace. But a curse from the sage Durvasa erased her memory so completely from his mind that he failed to recognise her. Much later, when the curse was broken he realised his mistake but it was too late....or so it seemed to be.

The story of Shakuntala first appeared in the Mahabharata. It was later adapted into a play by the Sanskrit dramatist ane poet, Kalidasa.

Script
Dolat H. Doongaji
and A. K. Lavangia

Illustrations
K. P. Shankar

Editor
Anant Pai

Cover illustration by: Pratap Mulick

SHAKUNTALA

MENAKA, A HEAVENLY NYMPH, LEFT HER NEW-BORN BABY NEAR SAGE KANVA'S HERMITAGE.

SHAKUNTAL BIRDS FLUTTERED ABOVE THE BABY. THE NOISE DISTURBED THE SAGE'S PRAYERS. HE LOOKED BEHIND AND SAW THE BABY.

THE SAGE PICKED IT UP.

I SHALL ADOPT THE BABY-GIRL AND CALL HER SHAKUNTALA.

THE BABY GREW UP AND MADE FRIENDS WITH THE ANIMALS AROUND HER.

TAKE MY ROBES AND ORNAMENTS. I WILL GO IN SIMPLE CLOTHES AND MEET THE SAGE.

WHEN THE KING HEARD VOICES, HE HID BEHIND A TREE.

OH PRIYA, HELP ME! THERE IS A BEE WORRYING ME.

LUCKY BEE! TO TOUCH HER LOVELY FACE.

CALL THE KING TO HELP YOU, SHAKUNTALA. IT IS HIS DUTY TO HELP HIS SUBJECTS.

PARDON US, SIR, WE HAVE VERY SIMPLE FOOD TO OFFER YOU.

PLEASE SIT DOWN AND HAVE SOME FRUIT WITH US.

WHILE THE KING WAS EATING, SOME HERMITS CAME ALONG.

WON'T YOU PROTECT US FROM THE DEMONS OF THIS FOREST? THEY DISTURB OUR PRAYERS.

DON'T WORRY, I SHALL REMAIN HERE TILL I DESTROY ALL THE DEMONS.

WE SHALL ALWAYS BE GRATEFUL TO YOU.

AFTER SOME DAYS WHEN THE KING WAS KEEPING WATCH FOR THE DEMONS, HE HEARD VOICES.

LET ME HIDE HERE AND LISTEN.

TELL US WHY YOU LOOK SO SAD, DEAR SHAKUNTALA.

HOW BRAVE AND GOOD OUR KING IS. I WISH I COULD MARRY A MAN LIKE HIM. BUT I AM ONLY A POOR VILLAGE GIRL.

SINCE YOU ARE SO SHY, WHY DON'T YOU WRITE TO HIM? HERE IS A LOTUS LEAF. WRITE ON IT WITH YOUR NAIL.

I do not know what you think of me, but I think you are the most wonderful man on earth

I MUST TAKE THIS LETTER TO THE KING.

A FEW DAYS LATER, A MESSENGER CAME.

YOUR MAJESTY, THERE IS URGENT WORK IN HASTINA-PUR AND YOU MUST LEAVE IMMEDIATELY.

I WILL COME AT ONCE.

I MUST GO NOW, DEAREST. WEAR THIS RING ON YOUR FINGER ALWAYS.

GOOD-BYE, SHAKUNTALA! I SHALL SOON SEND MY MINISTERS TO BRING YOU TO MY PALACE.

SOMETIME LATER, SAGE DURVASA PAID A VISIT TO THE HERMITAGE. SHAKUN-TALA WAS THINKING ABOUT HER HUSBAND.

WHERE'S MY FRIEND KANVA? DOES NO ONE WELCOME A GUEST IN THIS PLACE?

AFTER SOME WEEKS —

OH! WHEN WILL DUSHYANT SEND FOR ME?

IF ONLY FATHER KANVA WERE HERE, HE WOULD KNOW WHAT TO DO.

WHEN SAGE KANVA RETURNED TO HIS HERMITAGE, HE HEARD A HEAVENLY VOICE.

"O SAGE, REJOICE! SHAKUNTALA IS MARRIED TO A MAN WORTHY OF HER. SHE WILL SOON HAVE A SON WHO WILL BE A GREAT EMPEROR."

THE SAGE WAS WELCOMED BY THE GIRLS.

I HAVE HEARD THE GOOD NEWS. NOW WE MUST SEND YOU TO YOUR HUSBAND.

GAUTAMI, AN OLD LADY, WAS LIKE A MOTHER TO SHAKUNTALA. SHE MADE PREPARATIONS FOR SHAKUNTALA TO LEAVE.

OUR SHAKUNTALA DOES NOT HAVE CLOTHES AND JEWELS FIT FOR A BRIDE.

THE GODS ALWAYS HELP THE GOOD.

SUDDENLY A MIRACLE HAPPENED.

OH LOOK! WHAT LOVELY CLOTHES ARE HERE!

ON EVERY BRANCH THERE'S A SHINING JEWEL.

OH SHAKUNTALA, HOW LOVELY YOU LOOK IN THESE CLOTHES.

NOW THAT YOU WILL BE LIVING IN A PALACE, YOU WILL FORGET YOUR POOR FRIENDS.

I WILL NEVER FORGET YOU. I WILL COME TO MEET YOU OFTEN.

SAD AT PARTING, THE PLANT CLUNG TO HER.

TAKE CARE OF MY FAWN AND ALL MY OTHER PETS.

OH CREATURES OF THE FOREST! SAY GOOD-BYE TO SHAKUNTALA WHO ALWAYS LOVED AND CARED FOR YOU.

FATHER KANVA WAS ALSO SAD. THE TREES SHED TEARS IN THE FORM OF LEAVES. PEACOCKS STOPPED DANCING AND THE DEER FORGOT TO EAT.

DURVASA'S CURSE HAD WORKED. THE KING HAD FORGOTTEN SHAKUNTALA.

YOUR MAJESTY, SOME INMATES OF SAGE KANVA'S ASHRAM HAVE COME TO SEE YOU.

I WONDER WHAT THEY WANT WITH ME. SHOW THEM IN.

SAGE KANVA GREETS YOU AND HAS SENT SHAKUNTALA, YOUR WIFE, WHO WILL SOON BE A MOTHER.

THE KING LOOKED SURPRISED.

DON'T YOU REMEMBER YOUR WIFE, SHAKUNTALA?

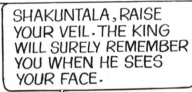

DO YOU REMEMBER HOW ONE DAY YOU COLLECTED RAIN-WATER IN A LOTUS FLOWER AND GAVE IT TO MY PET FAWN TO DRINK BUT SHE REFUSED.

YET WHEN I OFFERED IT, SHE DRANK IT GLADLY. SO YOU SAID — YOU ARE BOTH CHILDREN OF THE FOREST AND TRUST EACH OTHER...AND...

STOP YOUR CHATTER. I REMEMBER NO SUCH THING.

OH DUSHYANT! IT IS WICKED OF YOU TO DISOWN YOUR OWN WIFE.

SUDDENLY THERE WAS A BRIGHT LIGHT IN THE SKY. SHAKUNTALA'S MOTHER APPEARED.

WHO IS THIS HEAVENLY NYMPH?

THE NYMPH CARRIED AWAY SHAKUNTALA INTO THE CLOUDS.

THIS IS VERY STRANGE! I MUST TELL THE KING ABOUT IT.

A FEW DAYS LATER A FISHERMAN WAS ARRESTED IN THE BAZAAR.

LET ME GO! I DID NOT STEAL THIS RING.

YOU THIEF! IT IS THE KING'S RING. IT HAS HIS SEAL ON IT.

OH SHAKUNTALA! HOW CRUELLY I HAVE TREATED YOU. HOW COULD I FORGET YOU?

CALL THE CHIEF PRIEST.

WHERE IS MY WIFE SHAKUNTALA? WHO WILL BRING MY BELOVED BACK TO ME?

A NYMPH CARRIED HER AWAY AND SHE IS LOST FOR EVER.

TO LESSEN HIS GRIEF, THE KING PAINTED SHAKUNTALA'S PICTURE.

HERE IS LOVELY SHAKUNTALA IN THE GARDEN. HERE IS HER JASMINE CREEPER AND THERE IS HER PET FAWN...

FOR A FEW YEARS THE KING LED A QUIET LIFE THINKING OF SHAKUNTALA ALL THE TIME. ONE DAY—

GOD INDRA HAS SENT MATALI WITH A MESSAGE.

SHOW HIM IN.

THE GODS WANT YOUR HELP IN A WAR AGAINST THE DEMONS.

I AM READY TO HELP.

A TERRIBLE WAR WAS FOUGHT BETWEEN THE DEMONS AND THE GODS.

THE GODS WON THE WAR AND DUSHYANT CAME BACK TO EARTH IN MATALI'S FLYING CHARIOT.

WHAT LOVELY SCENERY! HOW HAPPY THE CREATURES OF THE EARTH LOOK. I ALONE AM UNHAPPY.

GOOD-BYE DUSHYANT! MAY THE GODS REWARD YOU FOR YOUR BRAVERY.

WHERE AM I? THIS IS A STRANGE PLACE WHICH I HAVE NEVER SEEN BEFORE.

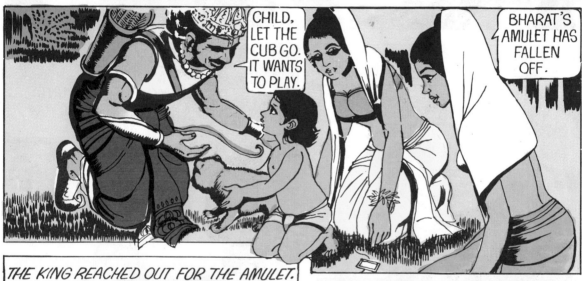

IT IS A MAGIC AMULET GIVEN BY SAGE MARICHA. IT WAS TIED ROUND THE CHILD'S ARM TO KEEP HIM FROM HARM. ONLY HIS PARENTS CAN TOUCH IT.

WHAT HAPPENS IF SOMEONE ELSE TOUCHES IT?

IT TURNS INTO A SNAKE AND BITES THAT PERSON.

THE KING RUSHED TO THE CHILD AND PICKED HIM UP.

OH, MY SON! MY SON!

DON'T CALL ME YOUR SON. THE GREAT KING DUSHYANT IS MY FATHER, NOT YOU.

LITTLE ONE, TAKE ME TO YOUR MOTHER, SHAKUNTALA. SHE WILL TELL YOU WHO I AM.

MOTHER, HERE'S A MAN WHO KEEPS CALLING ME HIS SON. HE WANTS TO SEE YOU.

OH DUSHYANT, SO YOU HAVE COME AT LAST.

The route to your roots

URVASHI

Urvashi's beauty takes King Pururavas' breath away. He is besotted. He forgets his duties as a king and is absent-minded with his wife, Aushinari. Both gods and humans are involved in the dramatic twists and turns of his romance with the charming apsara, who dances for Lord Indra himself. Eventually, stumbling through their highs and lows, King Pururavas and Urvashi finally find their way to everlasting joy.

Script
Kamala Chandrakant

Illustrations
Pratap Mulick

Editor
Anant Pai

URVASHI

URVASHI, THE PEERLESS CELESTIAL DANCER, WAS THE FAVOURITE OF INDRA. ONCE, AFTER DANCING IN THE HALLS OF KUBERA, SHE WAS RETURNING HOME ACCOMPANIED BY A FEW OTHER APSARAS.

SUDDENLY—

THE ASURAS CARRIED OFF URVASHI AND HER CLOSE COMPANION, CHITRALEKHA.

HELP!

HELP!

JUST THEN KING PURURAVAS, A FRIEND OF KING INDRA, PASSED BY IN HIS CHARIOT.

DEAR APSARAS, YOU LOOK TERRIFIED. WHO HAS DARED TO HARM YOU?

NOT US...OUR FRIENDS..... URVASHI AND CHITRALEKHA.... THE ASURAS HAVE KIDNAPPED THEM.

2

DO NOT WORRY. I WILL RESCUE THEM. WAIT FOR ME ON YONDER HILL-TOP.

PURURAVAS RODE OFF ON HIS MISSION.

AFTER A WHILE—

AH! REJOICE! THERE...KING PURURAVAS WITH OUR FRIENDS...

IN THE CHARIOT—

URVASHI, OPEN YOUR EYES. YOU ARE AN APSARA MAIDEN. SUCH TERROR DOES NOT BECOME YOU!

4

AS SOON AS THE CHARIOT TOUCHED EARTH—

PURURAVAS THEN ENTRUSTED THE BEVY OF APSARAS TO THE CARE OF A GANDHARVA.

TAKE THEM SAFELY BACK TO MY FRIEND.

AS THE GANDHARVA'S CHARIOT SOARED INTO THE SKY—

MY NOBLE KING, WILL I EVER SEE YOU AGAIN?

SWEET URVASHI, HAVING STOLEN MY HEART YOU ARE TAKING MY VERY BEING WITH YOU.

PURURAVAS RETURNED TO HIS PALACE AT PRATISH-THANA. BUT NOT FOR A MOMENT COULD HE TAKE HIS MIND OFF URVASHI. HE BECAME MOODY AND MOROSE.

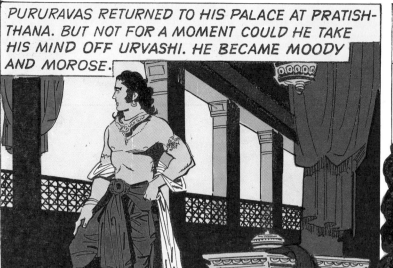

HIS FRIEND AND ADVISER, MANAVAKA, WAS CURIOUS.

WHAT AILS YOU, SIR?

PURURAVAS TOLD MANAVAKA ALL.

...AND NOW I AM SICK WITH LONGING FOR THE BEAUTIFUL APSARA.

YOUR QUEEN AWAITS YOUR PLEASURE. WHY DON'T YOU GO AND SEE HER?

PURURAVAS FELT GUILTY. HE HAD NOT SEEN HIS WIFE AUSHINARI SINCE HIS RETURN. HE HASTENED TO HER SIDE.

WELCOME, MY LORD! DID YOU MEET INDRA? DO THE ASURAS STILL TROUBLE HIM?

DEAR URVASHI, ALL WENT WELL. DO WAIT FOR ME TILL I FINISH SOME URGENT MATTERS OF STATE.

AND PURURAVAS LEFT.

AUSHINARI WAS HURT AND ANGRY.

HE CALLED ME URVASHI. ALAS! HAS MY HUSBAND FALLEN IN LOVE WITH ANOTHER WOMAN?

SHE SENT FOR HER FAVOURITE MAID NIPUNIKA.

NIPUNIKA, OF LATE THE KING HAS BECOME FORGETFUL. GO AND FIND OUT FROM HIS DEAR FRIEND, MANAVAKA, THE REASON FOR THIS AILMENT.

NIPUNIKA WAS SHREWD AND IMMEDIATELY GUESSED WHAT THE MATTER WAS.

MANAVAKA WILL NEVER TELL ME ANYTHING. I WILL HAVE TO TRICK THE TRUTH OUT OF HIM.

MANAVAKA MEANWHILE WAS IN AGONY.

HIS SECRET WEIGHS HEAVILY ON ME. I'D BETTER KEEP AWAY FROM PEOPLE LEST I BLURT IT OUT. I'LL WAIT HERE FOR HIM.

NIPUNIKA TRACKED HIM DOWN AS HE SAT WORRYING ABOUT KEEPING THE SECRET.

NOBLE SIR. THE QUEEN IS HEART-BROKEN AND CANNOT BE CONSOLED.

WHY ? HAS MY FRIEND OFFENDED HER IN ANY WAY ?

IT SEEMS HE ADDRESSED HER BY THE NAME OF THAT WOMAN FOR WHOM HE IS PINING

WHAT ! HE CALLED HER URVASHI ?

HE DID, NOBLE SIR! WHO IS URVASHI?

A CERTAIN APSARA. THE KING LOVES HER. HIS INFATUATION BOTHERS ME TOO.

SO THAT'S IT!

BUT WHAT SHALL I SAY TO THE QUEEN?

TELL HER I AM TRYING MY BEST TO DISTRACT HIM. I WILL NOT SEE HER TILL I'VE SUCCEEDED.

HARDLY HAD NIPUNIKA LEFT, WHEN PURURAVAS CAME TO MANAVAKA.

I TRUST YOU HAVE KEPT MY SECRET.

HAS THE WRETCHED GIRL SQUEALED?

SO WELL, THAT FOR A MOMENT I DID NOT KNOW WHAT YOU WERE TALKING ABOUT!

PURURAVAS WAS SATISFIED.

I DESIRE SOLITUDE. COME LET US GO TO THE ARBOUR IN MY GARDEN.

9

IN THE ARBOUR—

SIT HERE. LET THE SPLENDOUR OF NATURE FILL YOUR HEART AND DRIVE OUT ALL THOUGHTS OF URVASHI.

IMPOSSIBLE! SHOW ME INSTEAD, HOW I MAY CONTINUOUSLY FEAST MY THOUGHTS ON HER.

MEANWHILE THE LOVE-LORN URVASHI, ALONG WITH CHITRALEKHA, CAME DOWN FROM HER HEAVENLY ABODE, TO THAT VERY SPOT. BUT THEY REMAINED INVISIBLE.

HE IS HARD TO RESIST, IS HE NOT?

QUITE SO. COME LET US REVEAL OURSELVES TO HIM.

NO! NOT YET! LET ME OVERHEAR THEIR TALK.

AS YOU WISH.

MANAVAKA WAS BUSY ADVISING PURURAVAS.

THERE ARE TWO WAYS OF KEEPING YOUR DIFFICULT MISTRESS WITH YOU FOREVER.

URVASHI'S HEART SANK WHEN SHE HEARD THAT.

OH! WRETCHED ME. HE LOVES ANOTHER.

WHY! YOU GIVE IN TO JEALOUSY LIKE A MORTAL WOMAN. WE ARE CELESTIALS, REMEMBER. LISTEN FURTHER.

MANAVAKA MEANWHILE WENT ON WITH HIS ADVICE.

EITHER SLEEP AS MUCH AS YOU CAN, SO YOU DREAM OF HER, OR PAINT URVASHI'S PORTRAIT AND GAZE AT IT.

BOTH IMPOSSIBLE.

WHY?

MY YEARNING WILL NOT LET ME SLEEP; AND MY TEARS WILL BLIND ME BEFORE THE PORTRAIT IS HALF FINISHED.

OH! IF ONLY SHE KNEW HOW I SUFFERED. PERHAPS SHE DOES AND YET CHOOSES TO BE CRUEL.

CHITRALEKHA NUDGED URVASHI.

DID YOU HEAR THAT?

I CANNOT BEAR IT ANY LONGER. COME, FIND ME A LEAF AND I SHALL LET HIM KNOW MY HEART'S LONGING.

CHITRALEKHA BROUGHT HER THE LEAF AND URVASHI WROTE HER MESSAGE ON IT.

PURURAVAS AND MANAVAKA STARTED IN SURPRISE AS THE LEAF FELL BETWEEN THEM.

A LEAF? WITH WRITING?

PERHAPS SHE HEARD YOUR LAMENT AND HAS ANSWERED.

PURURAVAS READ IT AND HIS FACE LIT UP WITH JOY.

YOU ARE RIGHT. IT IS A DECLARATION OF HER LOVE.

YOU ARE CONTENT NOW, I HOPE.

PLEASE HOLD THE LEAF. MY CLUMSY HANDS MIGHT ERASE THE SWEET LETTERS.

BUT WHY DOESN'T YOUR MISTRESS SHOW HERSELF?

13

BUT AUSHINARI WAS HAUGHTY AND COLD.

I AM SORRY FOR FORCING MY UNWELCOME PRESENCE ON YOU.

SHE TURNED TO GO AWAY.

DEAR QUEEN, I'M GUILTY. PLEASE FORGIVE ME.

AUSHINARI WALKED AWAY, FOLLOWED BY NIPUNIKA.

AUSHINARI WAS IN TWO MINDS.

I SHOULD NOT BE WEAK-MINDED AND ACCEPT HIS HOLLOW APOLOGY. YET I CANNOT BEAR TO HURT HIM. BUT, NO....

WELL, SHE HAS REASON TO SPURN ME. THOUGH I LOVE URVASHI, I AM FOND OF HER TOO, AND HATE TO HURT HER. I WILL WAIT PATIENTLY TILL HER ANGER HAS COOLED DOWN.

MEANWHILE IN INDRA'S COURT, URVASHI'S DANCE WAS ON.

URVASHI PLAYED THE PART OF LAXMI. AS THE DANCE PROGRESSED—

OF ALL THE GODS ASSEMBLED HERE, TO WHOM DOES YOUR HEART BELONG?

PURURAVAS!

THE LOVE-STRUCK URVASHI HAD UTTERED THE NAME OF HER BELOVED INSTEAD OF REPLYING "PURUSHOTTAM." SAGE BHARATA, HER GURU, WAS FURIOUS.

YOU HAVE PUT ME TO SHAME! I BANISH YOU FROM HEAVEN.

AFTER THE DANCE WAS OVER, INDRA SAW URVASHI, HER HEAD BENT LOW, STANDING ALONE IN A CORNER. HE WAS MOVED.

YOU ARE MY FAVOURITE AND PURURAVAS IS MY GREATEST ALLY. YOU MAY GO AND STAY WITH HIM. BUT IF YOU BEAR HIM A CHILD, THE MOMENT HE SETS EYES ON IT, YOU MUST RETURN TO MY COURT.

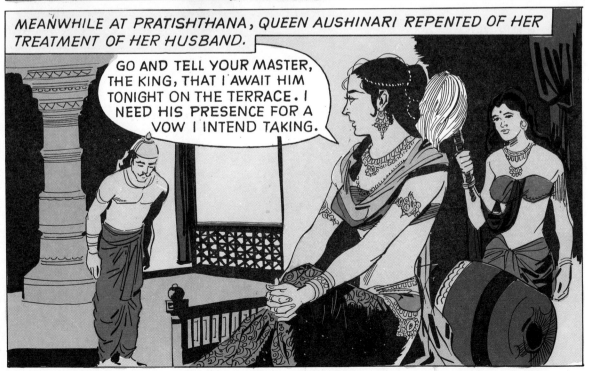

MEANWHILE AT PRATISHTHANA, QUEEN AUSHINARI REPENTED OF HER TREATMENT OF HER HUSBAND.

GO AND TELL YOUR MASTER, THE KING, THAT I AWAIT HIM TONIGHT ON THE TERRACE. I NEED HIS PRESENCE FOR A VOW I INTEND TAKING.

17

WHEN THE MESSAGE WAS GIVEN—

I SHALL CERTAINLY COME. I HAVE ALWAYS RESPECTED THE QUEEN'S WISHES.

PURURAVAS AND MANAVAKA ARRIVED ON THE TERRACE BEFORE THE APPOINTED HOUR.

LET US WAIT HERE FOR MY QUEEN.

AT THAT VERY MOMENT THE BANISHED URVASHI ACCOMPANIED BY CHITRALEKHA WAS ON HER WAY TO PURURAVAS.

LOOK! THERE HE IS ALONE WITH HIS FRIEND. LET US APPROACH HIM AND SHOW OURSELVES.

AS THEY WERE ABOUT TO PRESENT THEMSELVES TO PURURAVAS—

BUT THE QUEEN IS HERE.

BE CALM. THE QUEEN SEEMS DRESSED FOR SOME RITUAL. SHE WILL NOT STAY LONG. LET'S WATCH.

THE QUEEN ADVANCED.

WELCOME, MY QUEEN.

MY HUSBAND!

AUSHINARI'S REGAL BEARING AND EXQUISITE BEAUTY IMPRESSED URVASHI.

SHE IS MAJESTIC!

URVASHI'S SOUL IS PURE AND LOFTY. I'M PROUD OF HER.

AUSHINARI THEN TOOK HER VOW.

I, AUSHINARI, CALL UPON HEAVEN TO WITNESS MY VOW. I SHALL CLEANSE MY HEART OF JEALOUSY. HENCEFORTH I WILL WELCOME AS MY SISTER WHICHEVER WOMAN MY HUSBAND CHOOSES TO LOVE.

PURURAVAS WAS OVERWHELMED.

DEAR QUEEN! THIS VOW IS NOT NECESSARY. I AM NOT LOST TO YOU.

I HAVE TAKEN MY VOW.

SHE TURNED TO HER MAIDS.

LET US GO.

WAIT! DEAR ONE! DON'T LEAVE ME YET.

URVASHI WAS PUZZLED.

I DON'T UNDERSTAND ALL THAT IS GOING ON. BUT HER WORDS MAKE ME FEEL PURE AND FULL OF CONFIDENCE. I KNOW HE LOVES HIS WIFE AND YET I CANNOT BEAR TO GIVE HIM UP.

SHE'S GONE. OH! I WISH MY UR-VASHI WERE HERE NOW.

URVASHI WAS FILLED WITH A NEW BOLDNESS. SHE MADE HERSELF VISIBLE.

MY LORD! THE QUEEN HAS GIVEN YOU TO ME. I CAN NOW DARE TO LOVE YOU WITH ALL MY HEART AND BODY.

YOU ACCEPT ME BECAUSE MY QUEEN GAVE YOU PERMIS-SION. WHO PERMITTED YOU TO STEAL MY HEART?

URVASHI WAS TOO BASH-FUL TO ANSWER HIM.

COME LET US GO TO THE GANDHA-MADANA GARDENS.

URVASHI AND PURURAVAS SPENT MANY HAPPY SEASONS IN GANDHAMA-DANA.

ONE DAY PURURAVAS SAW A BEAUTIFUL GIRL BY THE BANK OF A RIVER AND GAZED LONG AT HER.

URVASHI WAS SUDDENLY SEIZED WITH A FIT OF JEALOUS ANGER.

MY LORD IS CHARMED BY ANOTHER. HE NO LONGER LOVES ME !

SHE TURNED UPON HIM IN ANGER.

YOU ARE WELCOME TO JOIN HER. I'M GOING.

URVASHI ! WAIT! BE REASON-ABLE.

BUT PUSHING HIM ASIDE, URVASHI RUSHED INTO A GROVE NEARBY.

SUDDENLY—

ALAS! ALAS! IN MY HASTE I'VE ENTERED THE WAR-LORD'S FORBIDDEN GROVE. O MY LORD! SAVE ME....

THE GROVE BELONGED TO KARTIKEYA, THE WAR-LORD AND WOMEN WERE FORBIDDEN FROM ENTERING IT. IF THEY DID, THEY WERE STRAIGHTAWAY TURNED INTO CREEPERS.

BUT ALL WAS NOT LOST. THERE WAS A WAY OUT, FOR KARTIKEYA HAD SAID—

IF A JEWEL FORMED OUT OF THE CRIMSON DYE DRIPPING FROM MY MOTHER'S FEET, TOUCHES THE WOMAN-TURNED-CREEPER, SHE WILL REGAIN HER OLD FORM.

PURURAVAS MEANWHILE SEARCHED IN VAIN FOR URVASHI. HE WANDERED AS ONE MAD, FOR SEVERAL DAYS, APPEALING TO ALL OF NATURE TO HELP HIM FIND HIS LOST LOVE.

22

PURURAVAS COULD NOT BELIEVE HIS EARS.

AT LAST SOMEONE HAS UNDERSTOOD MY PLIGHT. BUT WHO COULD IT BE?

AS HE LIFTED HIS EYES, HE SAW BEFORE HIM A FLOWERLESS, FORLORN CREEPER.

AH! POOR WAN CREEPER. YOU REMIND ME OF MY URVASHI.

NO SOONER HAD PURURAVAS ENCIRCLED THE CREEPER WITH HIS HANDS THAN—

WHAT TRICK IS THIS? I FEEL MY URVASHI'S ARMS. NO! I DARE NOT OPEN MY EYES AND FACE THE TRUTH.

INDEED, THE CREEPER WAS URVASHI.

MY LORD! OPEN YOUR EYES! PLEASE!

URVASHI! YOU! WHERE DID YOU GO? HOW COULD YOU HAVE TREATED ME SO?

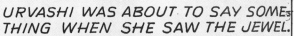

URVASHI WAS ABOUT TO SAY SOMETHING WHEN SHE SAW THE JEWEL.

THE JEWEL OF REUNION! NOW I KNOW HOW I REGAINED MY FORM AS SOON AS YOU EMBRACED ME!

SHE EXPLAINED IT ALL TO A BEWILDERED PURURAVAS. THEN—

COME LET US RETURN TO YOUR PALACE. YOU HAVE BEEN AWAY A LONG TIME. PEOPLE WILL BLAME ME.

ABSENT FOR LONG, THE KING RETURNED TO A JUBILANT WELCOME IN THE CITY.

WHAT A WELCOME! THE KING HAS AT LAST RETURNED. EVERYONE IS HAPPY.

MANAVAKA HAD ONLY ONE LAMENT.

IF ONLY THE KING HAD A SON AND HEIR, OUR CITY WOULD WANT NOTHING.

AS MANAVAKA MUSED THUS, A MAID RAN UP TO HIM.

ALAS! CURSED WRETCH THAT I AM. AS I WAS CARRYING THE MAGIC JEWEL FOR THE APSARA A VULTURE FLEW DOWN AND SNATCHED IT.

WHAT! THE JEWEL GONE? THE KING'S MOST PRECIOUS POSSESSION LOST? I MUST GO TO HIM.

THERE FLIES THE THIEF. WHY DON'T YOU SHOOT HIM DOWN?

I CANNOT. HE IS OUT OF REACH OF MY ARROW.

PURURAVAS CALLED HIS CHAMBERLAIN TO HIM.

THE THIEF MUST RETURN TO HIS NEST IN THE EVENING. TRACK HIM DOWN.

IT SHALL BE DONE, SIR.

AND THE CHAMBERLAIN LEFT.

BUT HE SOON RETURNED.

SEE WHAT I HAVE HERE. THE BIRD WAS SHOT DEAD BY THIS ARROW AND I HAVE RETRIEVED THE JEWEL.

WHOSE ARROW IS IT?

THE OWNER'S NAME IS CARVED HERE. BUT MY EYES ARE FEEBLE. I CAN'T READ IT.

WONDER OF WONDERS! THIS ARROW WAS SHOT BY AYUS THE SON OF URVASHI AND PURURAVAS.

MY FRIEND, A SON! WHAT MORE DO YOU WANT?

BUT THIS IS IMPOSSIBLE. I HAVE NOT BEEN SEPARATED FROM MY URVASHI FOR A SINGLE DAY EXCEPT WHEN SHE ENTERED KARTIKEYA'S GROVE. HOW COULD SHE HAVE HAD A SON I DIDN'T KNOW OF?

JUST THEN THE CHAMBERLAIN RE-ENTERED.

SIR, SATYAVATI, A HERMITESS FROM SAGE CHYAVANA'S ASHRAM WOULD LIKE TO SEE YOU. SHE HAS A BOY WITH HER.

BRING THEM IN AT ONCE.

AS THEY ENTERED—

WHY, HE IS A REPLICA OF YOU! HE MUST BE THE BOY WHO SHOT THE ARROW— YOUR SON.

HE MUST BE. HOW I LONG TO HOLD HIM IN MY ARMS.

29

SATYAVATI TOOK LEAVE OF PURURAVAS AND URVASHI AND WAS ABOUT TO GO WHEN—

MOTHER, TAKE ME WITH YOU.

I CAN'T, MY SON. YOU MUST NOW LIVE WITH YOUR FATHER AND REIGN AFTER HIM.

I WILL, MY SON. PEACE BE WITH ALL OF YOU.

THEN MOTHER, WILL YOU SEND MY PET PEACOCK TO ME?

WHEN SATYAVATI LEFT—

WHY, WHAT'S THE MATTER? THIS IS THE HAPPIEST DAY OF MY LIFE AND YOU GRIEVE.

I HAD FORGOTTEN MY-SELF IN A MOTHER'S JOY...

THEN URVASHI TOLD PURURAVAS ABOUT THE CONDITION LAID DOWN BY INDRA.

...NOW I WILL HAVE TO GO BACK. THIS IS MY LAST HOUR WITH YOU.

PURURAVAS WAS STUNNED BY HER WORDS.

HOW ENVIOUS THE GODS ARE. I WAS FULL OF HAPPINESS TO KNOW I HAVE A SON AND NOW THIS BLOW. MUST YOU GO?

MY GRIEF IS NO LESS IN THIS SEPARATION. BUT I AM BOUND.

I UNDERSTAND. YOU HAVE TO OBEY INDRA.

AS FOR ME, I SHALL CROWN AYUS KING, AND RETIRE TO THE FOREST.

JUST THEN A SUDDEN FLASH LIT THE SKY AND NARADA DESCENDED TO EARTH.

GREETINGS, LORD NARADA.

HAIL PURURAVAS, GREAT GUARDIAN OF THE EARTH!

MY RESPECTS, LORD.

MAY YOU TWO LIVE FOREVER IN CONJUGAL BLISS.

OH! THAT IT MIGHT BE SO. WHAT BRINGS YOU HERE, MY LORD?

I BRING A MESSAGE FROM MIGHTY INDRA. HE NEEDS YOUR HELP AGAINST THE ASURAS. HE DOES NOT WANT YOU TO RETIRE TO THE WOODS. HE HAS GIFTED URVASHI TO YOU FOR LIFE.

WHEN PURURAVAS AND URVASHI HEARD THIS —

IN ALL I AM INDRA'S GRATEFUL SERVANT.

THE PANGS IN MY HEART ARE STILLED FOREVER.

NARADA RETURNED TO THE HEAVENS. PURURAVAS LIVED HAPPILY WITH URVASHI TILL THE END OF HIS DAYS.

AMAR
CHITRA
KATHA

UDAYANA

LOVE OVERCOMES ALL ODDS

The route to your roots

UDAYANA

King Udayana was a lucky man. He was handsome and strong, and had the love of two beautiful princesses. He also had the undying loyalty of able ministers. They pulled every trick in the book to ensure that he overcame his enemies and won back, not only his vast kingdom, but the happiness he richly deserved.

Script
Kamala Chandrakant

Illustrations
H.S.Chavan

Editor
Anant Pai

Cover illustration by: Pratap Mulick

UDAYANA

UDAYANA, KING OF VATSA, HELPED BY HIS LOYAL OLD MINISTER, YAUGANDHARAYANA, HAD ELOPED WITH VASAVADATTA, THE DAUGHTER OF KING PRADYOTA OF AVANTI. HE TOOK HER FROM UJJAINI, THE CAPITAL OF AVANTI, TO KAUSHAMBI. HIS OWN.

AT KAUSHAMBI, UDAYANA FOUND TIME ONLY FOR HIS WIFE AND NEGLECTED HIS ROYAL DUTIES.

YAUGANDHARAYANA WAS WORRIED.

A POWERFUL ENEMY IN PRADYOTA—AN INDIFFERENT KING HERE...

AT THAT MOMENT RUMANVAN, ANOTHER MINISTER, CHARGED INTO THE HALL.

ARUNI'S TROOPS ARE CLOSING IN ON KAUSHAMBI— AND ON US.

THE KING! I MUST GET HIM AWAY TO SAFETY. HARNESS THE CHARIOT.

YOUR MAJESTY, WE MUST LEAVE FOR LAVANAKA IMMEDIATELY. THERE IS NO TIME TO EXPLAIN.

UDAYANA HAD FULL FAITH IN YAUGANDHARAYANA AND DID NOT QUESTION HIM.

RUMANVAN IS BRINGING THE CHARIOT.

SOON, UDAYANA, VASAVADATTA, RUMANVAN, YAUGANDHARAYANA, VASANTAKA (THE COURT JESTER) AND A FEW ATTENDANTS LEFT FOR LAVANAKA. ON THE WAY—

YOUR MAJESTY, ARUNI'S TROOPS ARE STORMING KAUSHAMBI.

LET THEM. RIGHT NOW MY HEART KNOWS NO STORMS. IT IS FULL OF LOVE.

SETTING UP CAMP AT LAVANAKA, YAUGANDHARA-YANA FOUND TIME TO RELAX, THINK AND PLAN.

THE KING IS IN A DAZE. I MUST DEFEND KAUSHAMBI AND REGAIN ALL LOST TERRITORY.

DARSHAKA OF MAGHADA COULD BE THE POWERFUL ALLY I NEED FOR THIS. HE IS AS MIGHTY AS PRADYOTA.

IT IS PROPHESIED THAT UDAYANA WILL MARRY DARSHAKA'S SISTER, PADMAVATI, AND ONLY THEN WILL ARUNI BE CRUSHED. IF ONLY OUR KING WOULD APPROACH DAR-SHAKA FOR HER HAND. BUT...

...BUT WITH VASAVADATTA BY HIS SIDE, UDAYANA WILL NOT HEAR OF THIS NOR WILL DARSHAKA RISK THE HAPPINESS OF HIS SISTER. I MUST HASTEN THE FULFILMENT OF THE PROPHECY.

THE MORE HE THOUGHT ABOUT IT, THE GREATER WAS HIS CONVICTION THAT HE NEEDED VASAVADATTA AS AN ACCOMPLICE.

O WISE QUEEN, I NEED YOUR HELP TO SAVE THE KINGDOM AND YOUR LORD, THE KING.

I AM MOST WILLING TO HELP. WHAT CAN I DO?

WILL YOU DO AS I SAY, ASKING NO QUESTIONS?

I HAVE FULL FAITH IN YOUR LOYALTY TO MY LORD AND TO ME.

YAUGANDHARAYANA THEN WENT TO RUMANVAN.

I HAVE A PLAN TO SAVE THE KINGDOM. WHEN OUR KING MARRIES THE PRINCESS OF MAGADHA...

NO. HE WON'T. NOT AS LONG AS VASAVADATTA IS ALIVE.

YAUGANDHARAYANA UNFOLDED HIS PLANS TO RUMANVAN.

WHEN I REMOVE VASAVADATTA FROM THE SCENE, PERSUADE THE KING TO VISIT MAGADHA WITH VASANTAKA. THEN RALLY OUR FORCES AND FOLLOW HIM.

A FEW DAYS LATER, WHEN UDAYANA WAS OUT HUNTING —

MY LADY, GO AND WAIT AT SOME DISTANCE FROM THE CAMP. I WILL JOIN YOU THERE.

YAUGANDHARAYANA THEN WENT TO RUMANVAN.

GET THE MEN OUT OF THEIR TENTS ON ANY PRETEXT. SAY YOU HAVE AN ANNOUNCEMENT TO MAKE.

AS SOON AS RUMANVAN HAD COLLECTED THE MEN AROUND HIM, YAUGANDHARAYANA SET FIRE TO VASAVADATTA'S TENT.

BY THE TIME THE MEN NOTICED THE FIRE, QUITE A FEW TENTS WERE ABLAZE.

FIRE! FIRE!

RUN!

THE QUEEN! WHERE IS SHE?

OH! NO! SHE WAS IN HER TENT.

YAUGANDHARAYANA DASHED TOWARDS THE TENT.

THERE GOES THE FAITHFUL MINISTER TO SAVE HER.

COME. LET US GO TO OUR TENTS AND SALVAGE WHAT WE CAN.

WHEN THE MEN WERE BUSY ELSEWHERE, YAUGANDHARAYANA CAME OUT FROM BEHIND THE TENT...

...AND WENT UP TO VASAVADATTA.

QUICK, MY LADY. FOLLOW ME.

THE TWO OF THEM SLIPPED AWAY, UNNOTICED.

MY LADY, YOU MUST NOT DISCLOSE YOUR IDENTITY TO UDAYANA OR ANYONE ELSE TILL I GIVE YOU PERMISSION TO DO SO.

I WILL LEAVE HER IN THE CARE OF THE PRINCESS OF MAGADHA ON SOME PRETEXT.

I WON'T.

A FEW HOURS LATER, UDAYANA RETURNED TO THE CAMP.

A FIRE! WHERE IS VASAVADATTA? WHY RUMAN-VAN, WHAT'S THE MATTER?

THE QUEEN AND YAUGANDHARAYANA HAVE PERISHED IN THE FIRE.

UDAYANA WAS BESIDE HIMSELF WITH GRIEF.

VASAVADATTA, MY DEAR QUEEN! THERE IS NO LIFE FOR ME WITHOUT YOU.

UDAYANA PICKED UP THE CHARRED REMAINS OF VASAVADATTA'S ORNAMENTS.

RUMANVAN TRIED TO CONSOLE HIM BUT DID NOT SUCCEED.

THIS WAS THE PLACE WHERE SHE SAT ENTRANCED AS I PLAYED THE VEENA FOR HER. THIS WAS THE PLACE WHERE WE HAD OUR FIRST QUARREL.

THE MINISTERS MET.

HIS QUEEN DEAD AND HIS KINGDOM LOST! OUR KING IS STEEPED IN GLOOM.

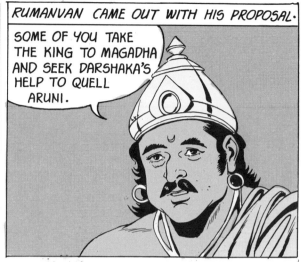

RUMANVAN CAME OUT WITH HIS PROPOSAL.

SOME OF YOU TAKE THE KING TO MAGADHA AND SEEK DARSHAKA'S HELP TO QUELL ARUNI.

LET VASANTAKA GO WITH YOU TO CHEER THE KING. THE REST STAY WITH ME.

THEY SUCCEEDED IN PERSUADING THE KING TO FALL IN WITH THEIR PLANS.

I HAVE DONE MY PART. THE REST IS UP TO YAUGANDHARAYANA.

MEANWHILE YAUGANDHARAYANA, DISGUISED AS A HERMIT WITH VASAVADATTA AS HIS YOUNGER SISTER, REACHED A FOREST NEAR RAJAGRIHA, THE CAPITAL OF MAGADHA.

LOOK, MY LADY, A HERMITAGE. LET US HALT THERE FOR THE NIGHT.

WHEN THEY REACHED THE HERMITAGE—

CLEAR THE WAY FOR THE PRINCESS.

THIS HUMILIATION IS MORE PAINFUL TO ME THAN ALL THE HARDSHIPS OF THE JOURNEY.

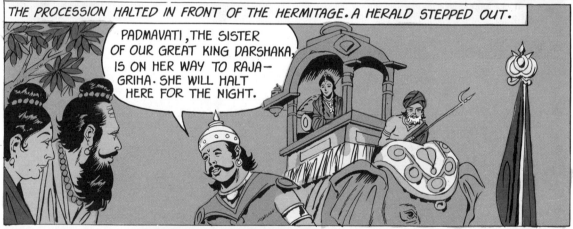

THE PROCESSION HALTED IN FRONT OF THE HERMITAGE. A HERALD STEPPED OUT.

PADMAVATI, THE SISTER OF OUR GREAT KING DARSHAKA, IS ON HER WAY TO RAJA-GRIHA. SHE WILL HALT HERE FOR THE NIGHT.

SO THIS IS THE PRINCESS, UDAYANA IS DESTINED TO MARRY. FATE HAS MADE MY TASK EASIER.

I AM DRAWN TO HER AS IF TO A SISTER!

AS PADMAVATI GOT DOWN FROM THE ELEPHANT AND APPROACHED THE HERMIT THERE—

SHE IS BEAUTIFUL AND HAS THE REGAL BEARING.

MAY YOU LIVE LONG. WELCOME TO THE HERMITAGE.

I SALUTE YOU, HOLY ONE.

YOU HAVE MADE ME FEEL AT HOME HERE. I AM GRATEFUL.

HER WORDS MATCH HER REGAL BEARING.

THE HERMIT THEN ADDRESSED THE MAID.

HAS NO KING YET SOUGHT THE HAND OF YOUR ACCOMPLISHED PRINCESS?

INDEED, YES. KING PRADYOTA OF UJJAIN HAS DONE SO; FOR HIS SON.

AH! THAT BRINGS HER CLOSER TO ME.

PADMAVATI MEANWHILE APPROACHED THE CHAMBERLAIN.

HAVE YOU FOUND ANY MENDICANT WHO WILL FAVOUR US BY ACCEPTING OUR GIFTS?

YAUGANDHARAYANA WHO WAS STANDING NEAR BY STEPPED FORWARD.

HERE IS MY CHANCE.

I SEEK A FAVOUR, NOBLE PRINCESS.

THANK YOU. YOUR REQUEST FULFILS THE PURPOSE OF MY SOJOURN HERE.

I WANT YOUR HIGHNESS TO LOOK AFTER MY SISTER, AVANTIKA, FOR SOME TIME. HER HUSBAND IS AWAY, AND I AM A MENDICANT.

I AM TO BE LEFT HERE! WITH THEM! I SUPPOSE THE WISE MINISTER HAS HIS OWN REASONS.

HOW CAN WE AGREE? HOW CAN WE TAKE THE RESPONSIBILITY?

IT IS IMPROPER TO WITHDRAW AN OFFER ALREADY MADE. WE SHALL TAKE CHARGE OF THE GIRL.

11

AT THAT MOMENT, THERE CAME A NEW VISITOR TO THE HERMITAGE, A WANDERING SCHOLAR.

OH! NO! A STRANGER.

WELL! WELL! SHE IS SHY OF MEN. MY WARD MUST BE SHIELDED.

KEEN ON GETTING TIDINGS OF THE OUTSIDE WORLD, YAUGANDHARAYANA QUESTIONED THE SCHOLAR.

WHERE HAVE YOU COME FROM AND WHERE ARE YOU GOING?

I AM ON MY WAY TO RAJA-GRIHA FROM LAVANAKA. I WAS A STUDENT THERE.

HAVE YOU FINISHED YOUR WORK AT LAVANAKA?

NO! I FLED LAVANAKA BECAUSE THE TRAGEDY THAT BEFELL THE VATSA KING, UDAYANA, LEFT THE VILLAGE DESOLATE.

WHAT WAS THE TRAGEDY?

IT'S A LONG STORY. LET'S ALL BE SEATED AND I'LL TELL YOU.

UDAYANA

WHILE THE SCHOLAR TOLD HIS TALE —

MY HEART IS SET ON MARRYING THE BEREFT UDAYANA. BUT WILL HE MARRY AGAIN?

AT LAST HE FINISHED.

WERE IT NOT FOR HIS GOOD MINISTER, RUMANVAN, THE KING WOULD SURELY HAVE GIVEN UP HIS LIFE.

DEAR HUSBAND, HOW DEEP IS YOUR LOVE! HOW I LONG TO BE SAFE IN YOUR STRONG ARMS.

PADMAVATI SAW THE TEARS ROLL DOWN VASAVADATTA'S CHEEKS.

AVANTIKA! TEARS IN YOUR EYES! YOU ARE TOO TENDER IN YOUR FEELINGS.

YOUR HIGHNESS IS RIGHT.

IF YOUR HIGH-NESS PERMITS, I WOULD LIKE TO GO NOW.

WON'T SHE BE SAD WHEN YOU ARE GONE?

NO. SHE WILL NOT. SHE IS IN GOOD HANDS.

YAUGANDHARAYANA LEFT. THE OTHERS RETIRED FOR THE NIGHT AND SET OUT THE NEXT MORNING FOR RAJAGRIHA.

13

A FEW DAYS LATER, UDAYANA, VASANTAKA AND A FEW ATTENDANTS REACHED THE COURT OF DARSHAKA.

WELCOME, O VALIANT KING. WHAT BRINGS YOU TO OUR KINGDOM?

I SEEK YOUR SUPPORT TO CRUSH THE UPSTART ARUNI.

DARSHAKA, LIKE MANY OTHERS BEFORE HIM, WAS AT ONCE IMPRESSED BY UDAYANA.

HOW SAD THAT THIS HAND-SOME, NOBLE KING, SHOULD HAVE LOST HIS WIFE SO TRA-GICALLY. I SHALL OFFER HIM NOT ONLY THE FULL SUPPORT OF MY ARMY BUT THE HAND OF MY DEAR SISTER, PADMAVATI, AS WELL.

MEANWHILE PADMAVATI, VASAVADATTA AND A FEW MAIDS WERE PLAYING IN THE PALACE GARDENS.

THERE. NOW IT'S YOUR TURN.

ENOUGH, AVANTIKA. I HAVE HAD ENOUGH. I AM TIRED.

AS THEY RESTED UNDER A TREE —

WHY DO YOU STARE AT ME SO?

WITH YOUR FACE FLUSHED YOU LOOK MORE BEAUTIFUL THAN EVER — YOU FUTURE QUEEN OF UJJAINI.

THAT FUTURE IS NOT TO THE LIKING OF OUR PRINCESS. SHE WOULD BE WIFE TO UDAYANA, THE VATSA KING.

WHAT! SHE WANTS TO MARRY MY OWN LORD.

WHY HIM?

BECAUSE HE IS CAPABLE OF DEEP LOVE.

AS IF I DON'T KNOW!

BUT, PRINCESS, SUPPOSING HE IS UGLY?

NOT AT ALL! HE IS THE HANDSOMEST IN THE LAND.

PADMAVATI WAS SURPRISED.

HOW DO YOU KNOW?

I ALMOST GAVE MYSELF AWAY AND BROKE MY WORD TO YAUGANDHARAYANA. THANK GOD I HAVE AN ANSWER!

THAT'S WHAT EVERYONE IN UJJAINI SAYS.

AT THAT MOMENT, A MAID CAME RUNNING TO THEM.

PRINCESS, YOU ARE BETROTHED TO UDAYANA, KING OF VATSA.

HOW IS THAT? HIS GRIEF WAS SO GREAT. COULD HE HAVE FORGOTTEN ME SO SOON?

HE CAME HERE YESTERDAY AND...

DID HE CHOOSE HER HIMSELF?

NO! HE CAME HERE ON SOME OTHER MATTER WHEN OUR KING OFFERED THE HAND OF OUR PRINCESS.

OH! HE IS BLAMELESS THEN.

THE MAID TURNED TO PADMAVATI.

COME AWAY, PRINCESS. THE DAY IS AUSPICIOUS AND THE WEDDING MUST TAKE PLACE IMMEDIATELY.

THIS THEN WAS THE MINISTER'S PLAN TO SAVE THE STATE; AN ALLIANCE WITH THE MIGHTY KING OF MAGADHA. I HAVE BEEN A VICTIM OF STATECRAFT.

VASAVADATTA KEPT AWAY FROM THE WEDDING FESTIVITIES.

ALAS! I HAVE NONE TO TURN TO. I MAY NOT RETURN TO MY PARENTS AND EVEN MY HUSBAND NOW BELONGS TO ANOTHER.

AFTER A WHILE, SHE WENT INDOORS AND TRIED TO SLEEP AWAY HER SORROWS.

THE NEXT MORNING, PADMAVATI, VASAVADATTA AND A FEW MAIDS WERE BACK IN THE GARDEN.

IT IS STRANGE. I HAVE HARDLY KNOWN HIM BUT EVEN A MOMENTARY SEPARATION MAKES ME MISERABLE.

WHAT WOULD SHE KNOW OF THE MISERIES OF SEPAR- ATION?

I WONDER. DID VASAVADATTA LOVE MY LORD AS MUCH AS I DO?

EVEN MORE!

PADMAVATI WAS ONCE AGAIN STARTLED BY HER VEHEMENCE.

HOW DO YOU KNOW?

I HAVE SLIPPED AGAIN. NEVER MIND.

IF SHE DIDN'T, WOULD SHE HAVE ABANDONED HER PARENTS FOR HIM?

SHE WOULD NOT, I SUPPOSE.

JUST THEN, ONE OF THE MAIDS SAW UDAYANA AND VASANTAKA APPROACHING.

LOOK! THE KING...

MY NOBLE LORD! COME, AVANTIKA. SINCE YOU ARE SHY OF MEN WE WILL HIDE IN THAT BOWER.

FROM WHERE THEY WERE, THE TWO PRINCESSES COULD LISTEN TO UDAYANA AND VASANTAKA.

GOOD! THERE IS NONE AROUND. NOW, MAY I ASK YOU A QUESTION THAT HAS BOTHERED ME?

SPEAK!

WHOM DO YOU LIKE BETTER? THE QUEEN YOU LOST OR THE ONE YOU HAVE NOW?

I WILL NOT ANSWER THAT QUESTION.

YOUR HIGHNESS, I AM YOUR FRIEND. CONFIDE IN ME.

WELL, I ADMIRE PADMAVATI BUT MY HEART— IT STILL BELONGS TO VASAVADATTA.

IN THE BOWER—

AND I HOPE IT WILL BE SO FOREVER! MY SUFFERINGS HAVE BEEN WELL REWARDED. MY ROLE NOW BEGINS TO BE DELIGHTFUL.

THAT WAS NOT VERY GALLANTLY SAID.

BUT PADMAVATI STOOD UP FOR HER HUSBAND.

YOU ARE WRONG. ALL THE MORE GALLANT IS HE. HIS LOVE IS NOT FICKLE AND IS WORTH WINNING.

YOU ARE TRULY A NOBLE ONE, MY FRIEND.

MEANWHILE, REMINDED OF HIS DEAD WIFE, THE KING WAS OVERCOME BY GRIEF. VASANTAKA WAS ALARMED.

YOUR HIGHNESS, YOUR FACE IS WET WITH TEARS! WAIT HERE. I SHALL FETCH SOME WATER.

PADMAVATI WAS DISTRESSED AND LONGED TO GO TO HIM. BUT—

MY LORD WOULD BE EMBARRASSED TO SEE US HERE. LET US SLIP AWAY.

YES. LET'S DO SO. NO. YOU GO TO HIM. HE IS DESOLATE. WE WILL GO AWAY.

AVANTIKA IS RIGHT. YOU SHOULD GO TO HIM.

BUT AFTER WHAT SHE HAD OVERHEARD, PADMAVATI WAS DIFFIDENT.

DO YOU REALLY FEEL I OUGHT TO?

YES. YOU MUST.

AS PADMAVATI WALKED TOWARDS UDAYANA, VASANTAKA RETURNED WITH THE WATER.

MY LADY! YOU ARE IN TIME. SOME POLLEN FLEW INTO HIS HIGHNESS'S EYES. THEY BEGAN TO WATER AND HIS FACE IS WET. PLEASE TAKE THIS TO HIM.

HE IS AS GALLANT AS HIS MASTER.

SHE TOOK THE WATER AND STOOD BEFORE UDAYANA.

GOOD-DAY, MY LORD! HERE IS THE WATER.

PADMAVATI, WEL-COME. PLEASE SIT DOWN. MY EYES ARE SENSITIVE TO POLLEN.

SHE IS NO DOUBT UNDERSTANDING, BUT THE HEARTS OF WOMEN ARE SENSITIVE. BE-SIDES SHE IS NEWLY MARRIED. THE TRUTH WOULD HURT HER.

TO SAVE THE KING FURTHER EMBARRASS-MENT, VASANTAKA CAME TO HIS RESCUE.

KING DARSHAKA AWAITS YOUR HIGHNESS. HE HAS ARRANGED FOR YOU TO MEET HIS FRIENDS THIS AFTERNOON.

THAT IS TRUE. COME, PADMAVATI. LET US GO TO THE PALACE.

A FEW DAYS LATER, VASANTAKA SAT MUSING ABOUT MANY THINGS.

THE GOOD LADY PADMAVATI HAS WON HIS HIGHNESS OVER. HE DOES NOT PINE AS MUCH AS HE USED TO, FOR HIS LOST WIFE.

SUDDENLY, A MAID CAME RUNNING UP TO HIM.

VASANTAKA, PRINCESS PADMAVATI HAS A BAD HEADACHE. WILL YOU INFORM HIS HIGHNESS.

I WILL. WHERE IS SHE?

THE MAID TOLD HIM. THEN —

I HAD BETTER GO AND INFORM AVANTIKA TOO.

VASANTAKA WENT IN SEARCH OF THE KING.

YOUR HIGHNESS, HURRY. LADY PADMAVATI IS ILL AND AWAITS YOU.

IS THERE NO END TO MY SORROW? FIRST VASAVADATTA WAS SNATCHED AWAY. MY WOUND HAD JUST BEGUN TO HEAL AND NOW PADMAVATI IS ILL.

21

MY LORD, IT IS ONLY A HEADACHE THAT SHE SUFFERS FROM. SHE WILL SOON RECOVER.

WHERE IS SHE? TAKE ME TO HER.

BUT WHEN THEY ENTERED HER ROOM —

PADMAVATI HAS NOT YET COME.

SIT DOWN, YOUR HIGHNESS. WAIT HERE FOR HER.

UDAYANA SAT ON THE BED. AFTER A WHILE —

HE HAS FALLEN ASLEEP. THE PRINCESS HAS NOT YET COME. I'LL GO AND GET MYSELF A BLANKET.

MEANWHILE VASAVADATTA, WHO HAD GOT THE MESSAGE, CAME THERE AND MISTOOK UDAYANA FOR PADMAVATI.

THE PRINCESS IS ASLEEP. I'LL SIT BY HER ON THE BED.

BUT VASAVADATTA HAD ESCAPED.

WAS IT A DREAM OR WAS SHE HERE?

JUST THEN VASANTAKA RETURNED.

FRIEND! I HAVE GOOD NEWS FOR YOU. VASAVADATTA IS ALIVE. I HAVE JUST SEEN HER. RUMANVAN MUST HAVE LIED TO ME.

IMPOSSIBLE! YOU MUST HAVE DREAMT OF HER.

BUT UDAYANA REFUSED TO GIVE UP THE BELIEF THAT VASAVADATTA WAS ALIVE.

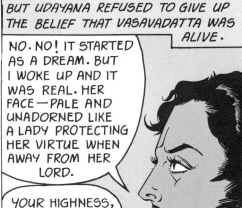

NO. NO! IT STARTED AS A DREAM. BUT I WOKE UP AND IT WAS REAL. HER FACE — PALE AND UNADORNED LIKE A LADY PROTECTING HER VIRTUE WHEN AWAY FROM HER LORD.

YOUR HIGHNESS, PLEASE. DO NOT MAKE YOURSELF AN OBJECT OF RIDICULE.

AT THAT MOMENT DARSHAKA'S CHAMBERLAIN ENTERED WITH A MESSAGE FROM HIM.

YOUR MINISTER RUMANVAN IS HERE WITH A LARGE ARMY. MY FORCES ARE AT YOUR DISPOSAL. GO. MAKE THE VATSA KINGDOM YOURS AGAIN. VICTORY TO YOU.

UDAYANA, NOW THAT HE HAD HOPES OF SEEING VASAVADATTA AGAIN, WAS FILLED WITH A NEW LIFE.

PLEASE CONVEY MY GRATITUDE TO HIS HIGHNESS. HIS HELP WILL NOT BE IN VAIN. I WILL NOT RETURN TO RAJAGRIHA WITHOUT DEFEATING THAT SCOUNDREL.

AND UDAYANA SET OUT TO WIN BACK HIS KINGDOM.

THE BATTLE WAS A FIERCE ONE.

UDAYANA'S ARMY EMERGED VICTORIOUS.

ARUNI HAS SURRENDERED. LONG LIVE UDAYANA, KING OF VATSA.

BACK IN HIS TENT —

RUMANVAN, MAKE ARRANGEMENTS TO LEAVE FOR RAJAGRIHA AT ONCE.

A TRIUMPHANT UDAYANA SOON RETURNED TO RAJAGRIHA.

UDAYANA

MEANWHILE, DURING THE WHOLE PERIOD WHEN UDAYANA WAS AWAY, VASAVADATTA HAD BEEN TORTURED BY MIXED FEELINGS.

IT IS GOOD TO KNOW THAT MY LORD WILL RULE IN GLORY ONCE MORE —BUT WITH PADMAVATI BY HIS SIDE! WHAT IS TO BECOME OF ME? HAS THE MINISTER FORSAKEN ME?

BUT VASAVADATTA HAD WORRIED UNNECESSARILY. A FEW DAYS LATER, AT THE PALACE GATES —

WE COME FROM UJJAINI. PLEASE TELL KING UDAYANA THAT A CHAMBERLAIN AND A MATRON FROM THE COURT OF THE MIGHTY PRADYOTA ARE HERE TO SEE HIM, WITH MESSAGES FROM THE KING AND QUEEN.

WHO ARE YOU?

WHEN THE MESSAGE REACHED UDAYANA —

COULD KING PRADYOTA HAVE HEARD THE NEWS OF MY MARRIAGE SO SOON?

PLEASE REQUEST PADMAVATI TO COME TO ME.

WHEN PADMAVATI CAME —

MY LORD, ARE MY RELATIVES IN UJJAINI WELL?

THEN YOU HAVE HEARD. IT IS NOBLE OF YOU TO THINK OF VASAVADATTA'S RELATIVES AS YOUR OWN.

MY LORD, IS IT PRUDENT TO HAVE ME SEATED BY YOUR SIDE? WOULD IT NOT PAIN THEM TO SEE ME IN THE PLACE OF THEIR BELOVED PRINCESS.

YOU ARE NOT ONLY NOBLE BUT THOUGHTFUL TOO. NO! YOU WILL SIT BY ME. I NEED YOU.

27

I HAVE SOME SLIGHT REASON TO BE NERVOUS. I ELOPED WITH THEIR DAUGHTER AND FAILED TO PROTECT HER.

THE FAULT IS NOT IN YOU. NO ONE CAN BE SAVED FROM THE CLUTCHES OF FATE.

AT THAT MOMENT AN ATTENDANT CAME IN.

THE VISITORS FROM UJJAINI ARE AT THE DOOR.

LEAD THEM IN AT ONCE.

WELCOME. WHAT BRINGS YOU HERE? I HOPE ALL IS WELL WITH HIS HIGHNESS AND THE QUEEN MOTHER.

THEY ARE WELL, MY LORD. MY KING SENDS HIS CONGRATULATIONS ON YOUR VICTORY OVER YOUR ENEMIES.

HOW GRACIOUS! I ELOPED WITH HIS DAUGHTER AND FAILED TO PROTECT HER. YET THE KING HAS ONLY GOOD WORDS FOR ME.

NOT ONLY THE KING, YOUR HIGHNESS, EVEN THE QUEEN.

WHAT DOES THE VIRTUOUS QUEEN HAVE TO SAY?

ACCEPT THIS PORTRAIT OF VASAVADATTA AND YOU, FROM US. WE HAD IT DRAWN TO SOLEMNISE YOUR WEDDING AS YOU DID NOT WAIT FOR THE RITES. MAY IT CONSOLE YOU. VASAVADATTA HAS PASSED AWAY BUT WE STILL HAVE YOU.

PADMAVATI WAS CURIOUS TO SEE THE PORTRAIT OF THE GIRL WHOSE DEATH HER HUSBAND MOURNED SO DEEPLY.

MY LORD, I WOULD LIKE TO SEE THE PORTRAIT, AND TO PAY MY RESPECTS TO MY ELDER SISTER.

THE MATRON SHOWED HER THE PICTURE. PADMAVATI WAS STARTLED.

SHE IS THE REPLICA OF AVANTIKA, MY COMPANION.

YOUR COMPANION, AVANTIKA? WHERE IS SHE? SEND FOR HER AT ONCE.

BUT SHE WILL NOT APPEAR BEFORE MEN. IT IS LIKE THIS...

PADMAVATI TOLD UDAYANA HOW AVANTIKA CAME TO BE IN HER CHARGE.

JUST AS SHE FINISHED, AN ATTENDANT CAME IN.

YOUR HIGHNESS, A MENDICANT OF UJJAINI IS AT THE DOOR. HE HAS COME FOR HIS SISTER.

29

IT IS AVANTIKA'S BROTHER, MY LORD.

YOU GO AND FETCH AVANTIKA. I'LL HAVE THE MENDICANT BROUGHT IN.

WHEN PADMAVATI TOLD VASAVADATTA THAT HER BROTHER HAD COME FOR HER—

THANK GOD! HE DID REMEMBER ME! NOW WHAT?

COME, I AM READY.

YAUGANDHARAYANA AND VASAVADATTA ENTERED THE ROOM AT THE SAME TIME.

YAUGANDHARAYANA! VASAVADATTA! THIS IS NO DREAM.

OUR PRINCESS! SHE'S ALIVE!

AVANTIKA— VASAVADATTA! NO!

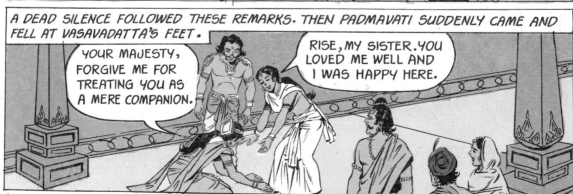

A DEAD SILENCE FOLLOWED THESE REMARKS. THEN PADMAVATI SUDDENLY CAME AND FELL AT VASAVADATTA'S FEET.

YOUR MAJESTY, FORGIVE ME FOR TREATING YOU AS A MERE COMPANION.

RISE, MY SISTER. YOU LOVED ME WELL AND I WAS HAPPY HERE.

"A Queen was kidnapped."

The King and his army went to her rescue.

If the **Ramayana** could be as simple as that,
it wouldn't have been an epic.

VASANTASENA

A DANCER AND HER MOST PRECIOUS JEWEL

www.amarchitrakatha.com

The route to your roots

VASANTASENA

Noble though penniless, the handsome Charudatta is the love of Vasantasena's life, but scoundrels and misguided friends threaten their happiness. Their tale, told by Shudraka in his Sanskrit play written 2,000 years ago, presents a picture of bustling town life at the time. Excitement and adventure lurk around every corner, and sudden twists and turns make this a classic nail-biting romantic thriller.

Script	**Illustrations**	**Editor**
Kamala Chandrakant	G.R.Naik	Anant Pai

VASANTASENA

PALAKA, KING OF UJJAINI, HAD COME TO THE THRONE ONLY BECAUSE HIS BROTHER GOPALA HAD ABDICATED IN HIS FAVOUR.

PALAKA WAS A TYRANT. MOST OF HIS SUBJECTS HATED HIM.

SHARVILAKA, PALAKA IS BECOMING MORE RUTHLESS, AND HAS GIVEN A FREE HAND TO HIS BROTHER-IN-LAW, THE WICKED SAMSTHA-NAKA.

NEVER MIND, MY FRIEND. BE PATIENT. IT IS PROPHESIED THAT ARYAKA, GOPALA'S SON, WILL SOON BECOME KING.

SHARVILAKA WAS A LEADER OF ARYAKA'S SUPPORTERS.

WE MUST SEE THAT THE PROPHECY COMES TRUE.

YES, YOU MUST JOIN US AND WORK FOR IT.

IN THAT SAME TOWN LIVED VASANTASENA A BEAUTIFUL, WEALTHY DANCER WHO OFTEN WENT TO THE TEMPLE OF KAMADEVA NEAR BY. ONE DAY—

AH! THERE HE IS AGAIN. THEY SAY HIS NAME IS CHARUDATTA. HOW NOBLE HE LOOKS.

SAMSTHANAKA CONTINUED TO CHASE HER.

SEE THAT RICKETY GATE. BEYOND IT LIES HIS EVEN MORE WRETCHED HOUSE.

WHAT! CHARUDATTA'S HOUSE! THE EVIL FELLOW HAS SHOWN ME MY REFUGE.

VASANTASENA RAN STRAIGHT IN THROUGH THE GATE.

HEY! WAIT! NOW WHERE DID SHE VANISH?

BUT BY THEN, VASANTASENA HAD ALMOST REACHED THE HOUSE.

MAITREYA, WHO IS THAT BEAUTIFUL WOMAN?

IT IS VASANTA-SENA. THE WHOLE OF UJJAINI KNOWS THAT SHE IS IN LOVE WITH YOU AND HAS REJECT-ED THE POWERFUL SAMSTHA-NAKA.

I AM TOO POOR FOR ALL THAT. SHE IS A FINE WOMAN AND IT IS WRONG OF SAMSTHANAKA TO TROUBLE HER WITH HIS ATTEN-TIONS.

CAREFUL, MY FRIEND. DO YOU WANT TO EARN HIS UNDYING HATRED? AH! THERE SHE COMES.

CHARUDATTA TOOK THE JEWELS AND GAVE THEM TO MAITREYA.

WHEN THEY REACHED THE GATE OF HER HOUSE —

AH! THERE GOES MADANIKA, MY FAITHFUL SLAVE. THANK YOU, SIRS.

FARE YOU WELL.

ONCE INSIDE, VASANTASENA CONFIDED IN MADANIKA.

NOW THAT YOUR JEWELS ARE IN HIS CARE YOU CAN MEET HIM OFTENER, MY LADY.

THAT HAS OCCURRED TO ME TOO.

HOW WELL I UNDER-STAND MY MISTRESS'S FEELINGS! MY LOVE FOR SHARVILAKA WOULD HAVE MADE ME DO THE SAME. HOW I LONG FOR THE DAY WHEN I MIGHT BECOME HIS WIFE.

MEANWHILE, CHARUDATTA AND MAITREYA WERE RETIRING FOR THE NIGHT.

ARE THE JEWELS SAFE?

YES! RIGHT UNDER MY PILLOW. WE MAY SLEEP IN PEACE.

THAT NIGHT A FIGURE STOLE QUIETLY INTO CHARUDATTA'S GARDEN. IT WAS SHARVILAKA.

PALAKA'S RULE MAKES ME A THIEF. MADANIKA, I KNOW OF NO OTHER WAY TO BUY YOUR FREEDOM AND TO MAKE YOU MY WIFE.

HM.M! THIS HOUSE IS OLD. THE WALLS ARE WEAK. IT MAKES MY TASK EASIER...

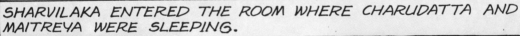

SHARVILAKA ENTERED THE ROOM WHERE CHARUDATTA AND MAITREYA WERE SLEEPING.

ALL ARE ASLEEP. BUT THE ROOM IS BARE. HAS THE RICH FACADE DECEIVED ME?

THE MASTER OF THE HOUSE SEEMS TO BE A LOVER OF MUSIC AND DANCING.

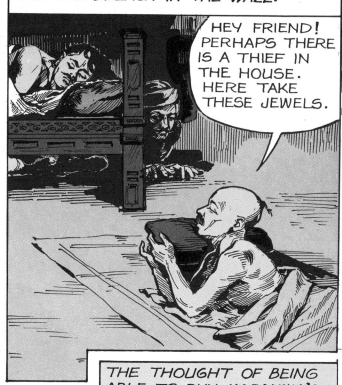

JUST THEN MAITREYA, HALF *ASLEEP*, SAW THE BREACH IN THE WALL.

HEY FRIEND! PERHAPS THERE IS A THIEF IN THE HOUSE. HERE TAKE THESE JEWELS.

IN THE DARK MAITREYA MISTOOK SHARVILAKA FOR CHARUDATTA.

I HATE WHAT I AM DOING.

THE THOUGHT OF BEING ABLE TO BUY MADANIKA'S FREEDOM STILLED HIS UNEASY CONSCIENCE.

BUT THIS WILL MAKE MADANIKA MINE.

8

ALAS! THEY HAVE BEEN STOLEN.

O RELENTLESS FATE! SO FAR SHE HAD ONLY DEPRIVED ME OF MY WEALTH. NOW SHE ATTACKS MY VERY HONOUR.

I CANNOT BEAR THE DISTRESS OF MY GOOD MASTER. I MUST GO AND TELL MY MISTRESS.

AFTER THE MAID HAD TOLD HER THE WHOLE STORY...

ALAS! ALL UJJAINI WILL SAY THAT MY HUSBAND, BECAUSE OF HIS POVERTY, HAS KEPT THE JEWELS FOR HIMSELF AND....

SEND MAITREYA TO ME.

ALL THAT I HAVE IS MY INVALUABLE PEARL NECKLACE. THE ONE MY MOTHER GAVE ME. IT WILL REDEEM MY HUSBAND'S HONOUR AND MORE.

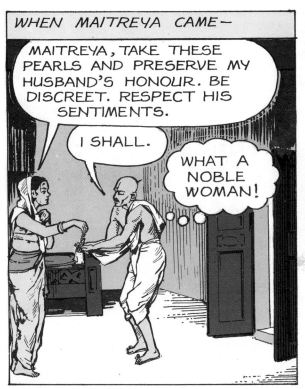

WHEN MAITREYA CAME—

MAITREYA, TAKE THESE PEARLS AND PRESERVE MY HUSBAND'S HONOUR. BE DISCREET. RESPECT HIS SENTIMENTS.

I SHALL.

WHAT A NOBLE WOMAN!

MAITREYA TOOK THE PEARLS TO CHARUDATTA.

TAKE THIS. FROM A DEVOTED WIFE.

I AM INDEED A RICH MAN. I HAVE A LOVING WIFE, A LOYAL FRIEND, AND MY HONOUR, WHICH A POOR MAN CAN SELDOM KEEP.

MAITREYA, GO TOMORROW MORNING AND GIVE THIS NECKLACE TO VASANTASENA.

MEANWHILE EARLY THE NEXT MORNING, SHARVILAKA WENT TO MADANIKA.

MADANIKA, I HAVE COME TO BUY YOUR FREEDOM.

FROM WHERE DID YOU GET THE MONEY?

AS SHARVILAKA CONFIDED HIS NIGHT'S ADVENTURE TO HER.

MADANIKA! MADANIKA! WHAT'S THE MATTER WITH YOU?

THE JEWELS BELONG TO MY MISTRESS. SHE HAD LEFT THEM IN HIS CARE.

BUT WHY?

MADANIKA THEN TOLD HIM OF HER MISTRESS'S LOVE FOR CHARUDATTA.

OH! HOW CAN I EVER STRAIGHTEN THIS OUT?

PRETEND THAT CHARUDATTA HAS SENT YOU TO MY MISTRESS WITH THE JEWELS.

12

SHARVILAKA, NOT KNOWING THAT VASANTASENA HAD OVERHEARD THE CONVERSATION, DID EXACTLY AS MADANIKA ADVISED.

....AND HE BEGS YOU TO TAKE THEM BACK.

SIR, IN RETURN I WANT YOU TO TAKE SOMETHING — MADANIKA.

B-BUT, I DON'T UNDERSTAND.

I DO; ONLY TOO WELL.

VASANTASENA THEN SENT FOR HER CARRIAGE.

GO MADANIKA. YOU ARE A FREE WOMAN, BUT DO NOT FORGET ME.

HEAVEN BLESS YOU.

13

AS SHARVILAKA AND MADANIKA RODE ALONG, THE KING'S HERALD WAS OUT ON THE STREETS MAKING AN ANNOUNCEMENT.

HIS MAJESTY, PALAKA THE KING, ORDERS ALL HIS GUARDS TO BE ALERT IN THEIR RESPECTIVE POSITIONS. ARYAKA, THE ONE PROPHESIED TO USURP THE KINGDOM, HAS BEEN CAUGHT AND IMPRISONED.

WHAT! ARYAKA IN PRISON! STOP!

ARYAKA HAS BEEN UNJUSTLY IMPRISONED BY PALAKA, WHO FEARS FOR HIS OWN SAFETY. I MUST GET OUT. I HAVE WORK TO DO.

OH! WAIT, MY LORD! WHAT WILL HAPPEN TO ME?

WHEN THE CARRIAGE DROVE AWAY WITH MADANIKA —

HARDLY HAD SHARVILAKA AND MADANIKA LEFT, WHEN MAITREYA CAME TO VASANTASENA.

TELL HER THAT I, WHO HAVE BECOME THE SLAVE OF HER HUSBAND, AM HER SLAVE TOO. THIS NECKLACE WAS MEANT TO ADORN HER NECK, AND SHE MUST KEEP IT.

BUT—BUT—ALL RIGHT, I SHALL DO AS YOU SAY.

VASANTASENA THEN REMOVED SOME OF HER OWN JEWELS AND TURNED TO THE BOY.

SON, TAKE THESE JEWELS AND DECORATE YOUR CART.

A MOMENT LATER THE MAID RETURNED.

MY MISTRESS WILL NOT ACCEPT IT. SHE SAYS IT WAS A PRESENT TO YOU FROM CHARUDATTA, WHO IS HER MOST PRECIOUS ORNAMENT.

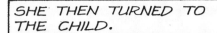

SHE THEN TURNED TO THE CHILD.

COME, MY SON, LET US GO AND PLAY. MADAM, I'LL BRING YOUR JEWELS TO YOU WHEN HE TIRES OF THEM.

A FEW MINUTES LATER CHARUDATTA ENTERED THE ROOM.

I AM SORRY I HAD TO KEEP YOU WAITING.

I WAS CONTENT TO WAIT.

NOBLE CHARUDATTA, YOU SHOULD NOT HAVE SENT THE PEARL NECKLACE TO ONE AS UNWORTHY AS I.

MY BELOVED VASANTASENA!

JUST THEN A CLAP OF THUNDER RENT THE AIR.

A STORM! I CANNOT PERMIT YOU TO LEAVE THE HOUSE TONIGHT.

THE NEXT MORNING —

I AM READY MUCH EARLIER THAN EXPECTED. AH! THERE'S THE CARRIAGE, WAITING FOR ME.

MISTAKING IT FOR CHARUDATTA'S CARRIAGE, SHE GOT IN.

WHEN THE CARRIAGE ARRIVED AT THE PARK ...

20

...TO VASANTASENA'S DISMAY, IT WAS NOT CHARUDATTA BUT SAMSTHANAKA WHOM SHE SAW.

ALAS! I GOT INTO THE WRONG CARRIAGE.

VASANTASENA! YOU! SO YOU DID COME TO ME. AND IN MY OWN CARRIAGE!

COME, MY DEAR. WE SHALL SHARE ALL THE PLEASURES THE PARK CAN OFFER US.

LET ME GO YOU EVIL ONE. IT IS NOT YOU I SEEK BUT THE NOBLE CHARUDATTA.

SAMSTHANAKA WAS VERY ANGRY WHEN HE HEARD THE NAME OF HIS RIVAL.

YOU SHALL DIE FOR THIS, YOU BEAUTIFUL CREATURE!

HELP! HELP!

21

SAMSTHANAKA TRIED TO STRANGLE VASANTASENA AND, BELIEVING HER TO BE DEAD, RODE OFF IN HIS CARRIAGE.

MEANWHILE ARYAKA HAD ESCAPED FROM PRISON.

THANKS TO SHARVI-LAKA, I HAVE ESCAPED. BUT WHERE CAN I GO NOW? I AM AN OUTLAW!

JUST THEN HE SAW CHARUDATTA'S CARRIAGE WHICH WAS WAITING FOR VASANTASENA.

THAT CARRIAGE THERE IS ABOUT TO LEAVE THE TOWN. I'LL GET INTO IT.

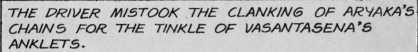

THE DRIVER MISTOOK THE CLANKING OF ARYAKA'S CHAINS FOR THE TINKLE OF VASANTASENA'S ANKLETS.

HER ANKLETS ARE QUIET. THE LADY MUST HAVE SETTLED DOWN. I SHALL DRIVE ON.

WHEN THE CARRIAGE ARRIVED AT THE PARK, THE EAGER CHARUDATTA STEPPED FORWARD TO HELP HIS LADY-LOVE OUT.

OH! OH! WHO ARE YOU, SIR?

I AM ARYAKA, THE SON OF GOPALA. I AM AT YOUR MERCY.

YOU ARE THE ONE WHOM KING PALAKA UNJUSTLY IMPRISONED!

I AM HE, SIR.

24

SAMSTHANAKA MEANWHILE WAS WORRIED ABOUT HIS DEED.

I HAVE MURDERED VASANTASENA. TO SAVE MY SKIN, I'D BETTER GO TO THE COURT AND PRESENT A CHARGE, ACCUSING CHARU-DATTA OF THE MURDER.

YES! THAT'S WHAT I SHALL SAY. CHARUDATTA, DISTRESSED BY HIS POVERTY, MURDERED THE WEALTHY DANCING GIRL, FOR HER JEWELS.

MEANWHILE CHARUDATTA HAD JUST RETURNED HOME.

SHE IS NOT HERE EITHER, THESE ARE HER JEWELS. WHAT ARE THEY DOING IN MY SON'S TOY CLAY-CART?

AT THE COURT AFTER SAMSTHANAKA HAD LODGED HIS CHARGE —

CLERK, GO TO CHARUDATTA AND SERVE HIM WITH THIS SUMMONS. HE MUST PRESENT HIMSELF AT THE COURT FORTHWITH.

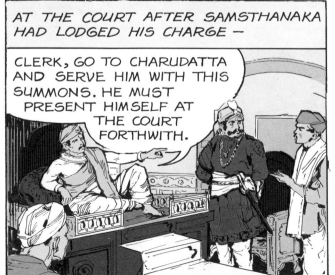

HE SENT FOR MAITREYA.

TAKE THESE JEWELS BACK TO VASANTASENA. SHE MUST HAVE GIVEN THEM TO THE CHILD TO PLAY WITH AND FORGOTTEN ABOUT THEM.

I WILL GO RIGHT AWAY, SIR.

WHEN MAITREYA HAD LEFT —

I HOPE MAITREYA FINDS HER AT HOME.

JUST THEN THE CLERK ENTER- ED AND SERVED HIS SUMMONS.

I AM BEWILDERED. WHAT DOES THE COURT SUSPECT? IS IT BECAUSE ARYAKA ESCAPED IN MY CARRIAGE?

WELL, I SHALL SOON KNOW.

COME, LEAD ME TO THE COURTROOM.

AT THE COURT THE MOMENT CHARUDATTA HEARD THE CHARGES READ OUT, HE LOST ALL INTEREST IN THE CASE.

WHAT! VASANTASENA MURDERED! WITH MY HONOUR LOST AND WITHOUT VASANTASENA, I HAVE NO FURTHER USE FOR LIFE. LET THEM DO WHAT THEY WILL TO ME.

MAITREYA, ON HIS WAY TO VASANTASENA'S HOUSE, HEARD THE NEWS ABOUT CHARUDATTA FACING A TRIAL FOR MURDER.

I SHALL GO TO THE COURTROOM RIGHT AWAY. VASANTASENA CAN WAIT.

AS THE CASE PROCEEDED, MAITREYA BURST INTO THE COURTROOM.

WHO IS THIS SCOUNDREL? HE HAS NO RIGHT TO DISTURB THE PROCEEDINGS.

AND SO CHARUDATTA WAS LED THROUGH THE STREETS, TILL THEY NEARED THE EXECUTION GROUNDS ON THE OUTSKIRTS OF THE TOWN.

MEANWHILE THE MONK AND VASANTASENA, NOW FULLY REVIVED, WERE RETURNING TO THE TOWN.

WHAT A LARGE CROWD! WHAT A COMMOTION! WHAT CAN THE MATTER BE?

THE MONK SUDDENLY STOOD STILL.

GOOD LORD! THEY SAY CHARUDATTA IS GOING TO BE EXECUTED FOR MURDERING YOU.

OH! WRETCH THAT I AM. QUICK! QUICK! LEAD ME TO HIM.

AS THE EXECUTIONERS WERE GETTING READY—

VASANTASENA, DEAD OR ALIVE, YOU WILL ONE DAY PROVE MY INNOCENCE. VIRTUE WILL TRIUMPH OVER EVIL.

30

AS IF IN REPLY TO HIS APPEAL—

STOP! STOP! I AM ALIVE. CHARUDATTA MUST NOT BE EXECUTED! HE IS INNOCENT.

AMAZING!

STRANGE

VASANTASENA ALIVE!

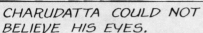

CHARUDATTA COULD NOT BELIEVE HIS EYES.

YES, CHARUDATTA! IT IS I, VASANTASENA, VERY MUCH ALIVE!

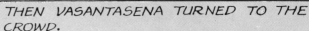

THEN VASANTASENA TURNED TO THE CROWD.

HEAR, ALL OF YOU. IT WAS THE EVIL SAMSTHANAKA WHO TRIED TO MURDER ME!

AT THAT MOMENT—

THERE COMES THE SCOUNDREL TO SEE IF HIS EVIL PLANS HAVE SUCCEEDED! KILL HIM!

NO, I BEG YOU, PLEASE SPARE HIS LIFE. THE PUNISHMENT HE NEEDS IS KINDNESS.

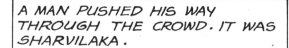
A MAN PUSHED HIS WAY THROUGH THE CROWD. IT WAS SHARVILAKA.

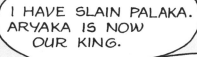
I HAVE SLAIN PALAKA. ARYAKA IS NOW OUR KING.

AH! THAT'S VERY GOOD NEWS.

KING ARYAKA HAS NAMED YOU VICEROY OF KUSHA-VATI. HE HAS ALSO CONFERRED UPON NOBLE VASANTASENA THE STATUS OF "SECOND WIFE TO CHARUDATTA".

WIFE TO CHARU-DATTA! AH HOW SWEET THE WORDS SOUND.

CHARUDATTA LED VASANTASENA TO HIS WIFE WHO WELCOMED THE TALENTED YOUNG DANCER.

MAITREYA HAS GIVEN US THE GOOD NEWS. WELCOME, LITTLE SISTER. YOU HAVE BROUGHT GOOD FORTUNE TO OUR HUSBAND AND HIS HOUSEHOLD.

I MUST HASTEN TO MADANIKA, WHO MUST BE ANXIOUSLY WAITING FOR ME.

RATNAVALI

A ROYAL PROPHESY IS HAPPILY FULFILLED

The route to your roots

RATNAVALI

King Udayana was in a dilemma: he had won the love of the beautiful Ratnavali, but how could he break the heart of his queen, Vasavadatta? Was a chance shipwreck going to wreck the peace and happiness of his home as well? Sagacious statesmen, loyal friends and even talking birds help in a romance which reveals all the subtleties of palace life so familiar to that master playwright, the 7th-century poet-king Harsha of Kanauj.

Script	Illustrations	Editor
Subba Rao	Pratap Mulick	Anant Pai

RATNAVALI

PRINCESS RATNAVALI, THE DAUGHTER OF VIKRAMABAHU, KING OF SIMHALA, WAS GOING TO KAUSHAMBI TO MARRY KING UDAYANA.

VASUBHUTI, THE KING'S MINISTER, WHO WAS ESCORTING RATNAVALI, TURNED TO BABHRAVYA, THE ENVOY FROM KAUSHAMBI.

OUR KING WAS SAD TO HEAR THAT HIS NIECE, KING UDAYANA'S QUEEN, VASAVADATTA, DIED IN THE FIRE AT LAVANAKA.

SO KING VIKRAMA-BAHU BELIEVES THE RUMOUR SPREAD BY THE MINISTER YAUGANDHARAYANA!

TO KEEP THE RELATION-SHIP BETWEEN THE TWO FAMILIES ALIVE, HE HAS AGREED TO SEND OUR PRINCESS TO KAUSHAMBI.

HOW WILL HE REACT WHEN HE DISCOVERS THAT VASAVADATTA IS VERY MUCH ALIVE?

1

YOUNG RATNAVALI WAS THINKING ABOUT VASAVADATTA AND KING UDAYANA.

MY COUSIN, WHOM I HAVE NEVER MET, IS DEAD. THE KING LOVED HER DEEPLY. WILL I BE ABLE TO WIN HIS HEART?

SUDDENLY—

WHAT'S HAPPENING? THE SHIP HAS STARTED TO ROLL!

A SUDDEN STORM HAD BEGUN. THE HUGE WAVES TOSSED THE SHIP ABOUT...

HELP!

...AND IT BROKE INTO A THOUSAND PIECES.

OH GOD!

RATNAVALI· MANAGED TO CLUTCH A PLANK···

··· AND KEEP AFLOAT.

THERE IS NOT A SOUL IN SIGHT! WHAT SHALL I DO?

FORTUNATELY, SOON AFTER, SHE SPOTTED ANOTHER SHIP.

HELP!

THE MASTER OF THE SHIP, A MERCHANT WHO WAS SAILING TO KAUSHAMBI, HEARD THE CRY.

A GIRL IN DISTRESS!

HE ORDERED THE SHIP TO TURN AROUND TOWARDS HER···

...AND HELPED HER ABOARD.

WHO ARE YOU?

RATNAVALI REMAINED SILENT.

HOW CAN I TELL HIM THAT I AM THE PRINCESS OF SIMHALA? SEEING ME IN MY PRESENT STATE, WOULD HE BELIEVE ME?

WHY DOESN'T SHE ANSWER? IS SHE SUFFERING FROM A LOSS OF MEMORY?

ANYWAY FROM THE NECKLACE OF PRECIOUS STONES SHE IS WEARING, IT IS CLEAR THAT SHE IS A LADY OF NOBLE BIRTH.

MEANWHILE AT KAUSHAMBI, YAUGANDHARAYANA, KING UDAYANA'S LOYAL MINISTER, WAS ANXIOUSLY PACING UP AND DOWN HIS CHAMBER.

PRINCESS RATNAVALI WILL SOON BE HERE. AND I HAVE NOT YET SPOKEN TO THE KING ABOUT HER.

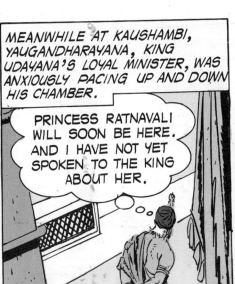

HE LOVES VASAVADATTA TOO MUCH. HE WILL NOT AGREE TO MARRY ANOTHER WOMAN AND YET....

JUST THEN A GUARD ENTERED.

SIR, A MERCHANT WANTS TO MEET YOU.

BRING HIM IN.

THE MERCHANT WALKED IN, BRINGING RATNAVALI WITH HIM.

SIR, I RESCUED THIS LADY FROM A SHIP-WRECK. I DON'T KNOW WHO SHE IS, BUT COULD I ENTRUST HER TO YOUR CARE?

THAT NECKLACE! SHE MUST BE RATNAVALI!

I WILL NOT LET HER SEE THAT I KNOW WHO SHE IS. I WILL TAKE HER TO THE QUEEN AND....

YAUGANDHARAYANA TOOK RATNAVALI TO QUEEN VASAVADATTA'S CHAMBERS.

O QUEEN, THIS IS SAGARIKA. SHE HAS NO ONE TO TURN TO MAY I ENTRUST HER TO YOUR CARE?

QUEEN VASAVADATTA LOOKED AFFECTIONATELY AT THE GIRL.

SHE WILL BE MY COMPANION.

YOU ARE VERY KIND. PERMIT ME TO TAKE YOUR LEAVE.

VASAVADATTA DID NOT KNOW THAT SAGARIKA WAS NONE OTHER THAN RATNAVALI, HER COUSIN.

AS YAUGANDHA-RAYANA LEFT—

EXCELLENT! RATNAVALI IS NOW BOUND TO COME ACROSS THE KING AND THEN I WILL LET MATTERS TAKE THEIR OWN COURSE.

SAGARIKA IS VERY CHARMING! I SHOULD TAKE CARE THAT THE KING DOESN'T MEET HER.

VASAVADATTA TURNED TO SAGARIKA.

MY FRIEND, I WANT YOU TO BE HAPPY HERE. YOU SHALL BE IN CHARGE OF MEDHAVINI, OUR BELOVED TALKING-BIRD. SUSANGATA WILL SHOW YOU WHERE IT IS.

SAGARIKA WAS HAPPY AND ENJOYED HER LIGHT DUTIES.

THE QUEEN IS KIND AND GENTLE.

THEN CAME THE FESTIVAL OF MADANA, THE GOD OF LOVE.

SAGARIKA, TODAY THE QUEEN WILL WORSHIP MADANA IN THE GARDEN.

O SUSANGATA, I WOULD LOVE TO BE THERE, BUT I HAVE TO LOOK AFTER MEDHAVINI.

I WILL DO THAT FOR YOU, SAGARIKA. GO AND ATTEND THE CEREMONY.

SUSANGATA, YOU ARE SO GOOD.

SO CARRYING MATERIALS FOR WORSHIP, SAGARIKA FOLLOWED THE QUEEN INTO THE GARDEN.

MEANWHILE, PEOPLE WERE OUT IN THE STREETS, CELEBRATING THE FESTIVAL BY THROWING COLOURS AT ONE ANOTHER. FROM THE PALACE KING UDAYANA WATCHED THE MERRY-MAKING WITH VASANTAKA, THE COURT JESTER

JUST THEN TWO OF THE QUEEN'S MAIDS ENTERED.

VICTORY TO YOUR MAJESTY! THE QUEEN COMMANDS... NO, NO... THE QUEEN REQUESTS....

THE WORD 'COMMANDS' IS MORE APPROPRIATE ON MADANA'S FESTIVAL. TELL ME WHAT THE QUEEN COMMANDS.

THE QUEEN REQUESTS YOUR PRESENCE AT MAKARANDA GARDEN WHERE SHE WILL BE WORSHIPPING THE GOD OF LOVE.

WE WILL COME AT ONCE.

WHEN THE KING REACHED THE GARDEN—

FRIEND, FLOWERS ARE IN BLOOM AND THE HUMMING OF BEES SOUNDS LIKE THE JINGLE OF WOMEN'S ANKLETS.

YOU ARE RIGHT, VASANTAKA. I SEE THEM COMING.

THAT SOUND IS NOT CAUSED BY BEES BUT BY THE ANKLETS OF THE QUEEN'S COMPANIONS!

MEANWHILE VASAVADATTA HAD APPROACHED THE RED ASHOKA TREE.

BRING ME THE MATERIALS FOR WORSHIP.

SAGARIKA STEPPED FORWARD.

HERE THEY ARE, YOUR MAJESTY.

HOW DID SAGARIKA GET HERE? THE KING MUST NOT SEE HER!

YES, YOUR MAJESTY.

SAGARIKA, YOU SHOULD NOT HAVE LEFT MEDHAVINI. GIVE THAT TRAY TO KANCHANA MALA AND GO BACK.

SAGARIKA LEFT RELUCTANTLY.

SO I WON'T BE PRESENT WHILE MADANA IS WORSHIPPED.

I CAN'T BEAR TO MISS THE RITUAL. I'LL HIDE HERE AND WATCH IT.

IN FACT, I COULD PICK SOME FLOWERS AND OFFER THEM TO THE GOD OF LOVE FROM HERE.

WHILE SAGARIKA WAS GATHERING FLOWERS, THE QUEEN WORSHIPPED MADANA.

THEN SHE TURNED TO UDAYANA WHO HAD JUST JOINED HER.

MY LORD, PLEASE SIT HERE AND ACCEPT MY WORSHIP.

AS YOU COMMAND, DEAR.

SUDDENLY SAGARIKA SAW THE KING—

OH! IN THIS COUNTRY MADANA COMES IN PERSON TO BE WORSHIPPED. IN MY COUNTRY WE HAVE ONLY HIS IMAGE TO WORSHIP!

THEN SAGARIKA OFFERED HER FLOWERS FROM WHERE SHE STOOD.

SALUTATIONS TO YOU, MADANA! MAY THIS VISION OF YOU BRING JOY TO MY LIFE!

THEN, AS SHE SET OUT FOR THE PALACE, SHE HEARD A GUARD CALLING OUT—

...MANY PRINCES ARE WAITING TO PAY THEIR RESPECTS TO KING UDAYANA...

WHAT!

SAGARIKA TURNED BACK.

SO THAT WAS KING UDAYANA AND I AM BETROTHED TO HIM! THEN THE QUEEN MUST BE MY COUSIN, VASAVA-DATTA!

BUT IT CAN'T BE! VASAVADATTA DIED IN THE FIRE····

AS UDAYANA AND VASAVADATTA PASSED BY—

HOW HELPLESS I AM. I CAN'T EVEN LOOK UPON HIM, LET ALONE TALK TO HIM.

UDAYANA'S FACE HAUNTED SAGARIKA AND SHE HARDLY SLEPT THAT NIGHT. THE NEXT MORNING SHE WENT TO THE GARDEN HOUSE TAKING WITH HER A DRAWING BOARD, BRUSHES AND COLOURS.

I SAW HIM BUT FOR A MOMENT. YET MY HEART YEARNS FOR HIM.

AS SHE SAT DOWN AND PAINTED A PICTURE OF KING UDAYANA FROM MEMORY···

···SUSANGATA CREPT UP FROM BEHIND HER—

WHAT ARE YOU PAINTING, SAGARIKA?

SAGARIKA BLUSHED.

HOW CAN I TELL HER THE TRUTH?

NOW THAT MADANA'S FESTIVAL IS BEING CELEBRATED I HAVE DRAWN THE GOD OF LOVE.

YOU HAVE DRAWN MADANA WITHOUT HIS CONSORT, RATI, BY HIS SIDE!

LOOK, I WILL DRAW RATI HERE.

WHY, YOU'VE DRAWN MY PORTRAIT!

SUSANGATA LAUGHED MERRILY.

DON'T GET UPSET, DEAR. IF THE ONE YOU HAVE PAINTED IS MADANA THEN THE ONE I'VE PAINTED IS RATI.

SUSANGATA HAS DISCOVERED MY SECRET....

NOW TELL ME ALL.

I AM OVERCOME BY A SENSE OF SHAME. YOU MUSTN'T TELL ANYONE ABOUT THIS.

YOUR SECRET IS SAFE WITH ME. BUT THIS TALKING BIRD MAY BLURT OUT EVERYTHING...

BUT SAGARIKA DID NOT SEEM TO HEAR SUSANGATA'S WORDS.

I HAVE LOST MY HEART TO ONE WHO IS UNATTAINABLE! DEATH CAN BE MY ONLY REFUGE.

SAGARIKA, TAKE HEART.

JUST THEN, A FEROCIOUS MONKEY CAME BOUNDING IN.

LET'S RUN, SAGARIKA!

ATTRACTED BY THE FOOD IN THE CAGE, THE MONKEY OPENED IT. THE FRIGHTENED BIRD FLEW OUT.

MEANWHILE OUTSIDE—

SUSANGATA, SOMEONE MAY SEE THE DRAWING. WE SHOULD HAVE RUBBED IT OFF.

YOU HAVE SOMETHING MORE SERIOUS THAN THAT TO WORRY ABOUT. LOOK! MEDHAVINI HAS FLOWN AWAY.

AND WHAT IS WORSE, SHE HAS HEARD EVERY WORD WE UTTERED. WE MUST CATCH HER.

MEANWHILE, UDAYANA ACCOMPANIED BY VASANTAKA, WAS ON HIS WAY TO THE GARDEN, WHEN VASANTAKA STOPPED ABRUPTLY.

THERE IS A GHOST IN THIS BAKULA TREE. LET'S RUN AWAY.

WHAT NONSENSE!

BUT DO LISTEN. SOMEONE IS SPEAKING, YET NO ONE CAN BE SEEN. THE BODY-LESS ONE IS THE GHOST!

LOOK! IT'S ONLY A TALKING BIRD!

WHAT!

O SILLY BIRD, DID YOU THINK I WAS REALLY AFRAID OF YOU? WAIT, I WILL KNOCK YOU DOWN FROM THIS BAKULA TREE.

FOOL! SHE IS SAYING SOME-THING PLEASANT. LET'S LISTEN.

WHEN THEY ENTERED THE GARDEN HOUSE—

17

MEANWHILE SAGARIKA AND SUSANGATA NOT FINDING THE BIRD, WERE RETURNING TO THE GARDEN HOUSE FOR THE PAINTING.

IT IS YOUR PORTRAIT! AND THAT OF A MAIDEN TOO!

THAT IS VASANTAKA SPEAKING. THE KING MUST BE HERE, TOO. LET'S HIDE AND LISTEN TO THEM.

MEANWHILE UDAYANA HAD TAKEN THE PAINTING.

O UDAYANA, YOU SEEM SPELLBOUND! WHY DOES THE PORTRAIT HOLD SUCH FASCINATION FOR YOU?

SAGARIKA HELD HER BREATH.

MY LIFE DEPENDS ON HIS ANSWER. WHAT WILL HE SAY?

THIS MAIDEN EXCELS LAKSHMI IN GRACE. SHE HAS CAPTIVATED MY HEART.

HOW SOOTHING HIS WORDS ARE!

I MUST FIND A WAY OF BRINGING THE KING AND MY FRIEND TOGETHER.

SAGARIKA, WAIT HERE. I WILL GO AND GET THE PORTRAIT.

ALL RIGHT, BUT PLEASE COME BACK SOON.

SUSANGATA WENT INTO THE GARDEN HOUSE AND CAME OUT AFTER A LITTLE WHILE WITH THE KING AND VASANTAKA.

THE KING IS COMING THIS WAY! I HOPE SUSANGATA HASN'T TOLD HIM IT WAS I WHO DREW HIS PORTRAIT.

HOW I HAVE BEEN LONGING TO MEET HIM! AND YET NOW I AM UNABLE TO TAKE A SINGLE STEP TOWARDS HIM.

THE KING APPROACHED SAGARIKA AND HE WAS ABOUT TO TAKE HER HAND IN HIS, WHEN—

QUEEN VASAVADATTA!

THE TWO GIRLS LEFT AT ONCE.

I WAS ONLY JOKING, MY FRIEND. WHY DID YOU LET THEM GO?

BECAUSE, UNWITTINGLY, YOU SPOKE THE TRUTH. THE QUEEN IS INDEED APPROACHING.

QUICK, CONCEAL THE PORTRAIT.

BUT THE CLUMSY VASANTAKA DROPPED THE PORTRAIT.

MY LORD, I CAME THIS WAY TO SEE IF THE NAVAMALIKA CREEPER HAS BLOSSOMED.

LET'S GO TOGETHER.

KANCHANA MALA, THE QUEEN'S COMPANION, PICKED UP THE PORTRAIT AND SHOWED IT TO THE QUEEN.

IT'S MY LORD AND SAGARIKA!

MY LORD, WHO HAS DRAWN THIS?

I TOLD THE KING THAT A SELF-PORTRAIT IS DIFFICULT TO DO. HE DISAGREED — AND TO PROVE HIS POINT HE DREW HIS OWN PORTRAIT.

AND THE GIRL?

I CONJURED THE GIRL OUT OF MY IMAGINATION.

MY LORD, ALLOW ME TO TAKE MY LEAVE OF YOU. I HAVE A BAD HEADACHE.

VASAVADATTA, ARE YOU ANGRY WITH ME?

NO, MY LORD. BELIEVE ME, I AM TROUBLED BY A HEADACHE. PLEASE LET ME GO.

THANK GOD! THE UNTIMELY HURRICANE HAS PASSED, LEAVING US UNHARMED!

THE NEXT DAY VASANTAKA MET SUSANGATA.

SUSANGATA, MY FRIEND PINES FOR SAGARIKA. CAN'T YOU DO SOMETHING ABOUT IT?

THIS EVENING I WILL BRING SAGARIKA TO THE MADHAVI BOWER, DRESSED IN THE QUEEN'S ROBES AND I MYSELF WILL BE IN KANCHANA MALA'S DRESS.

LITTLE DID THEY REALISE THAT KANCHANA MALA, WHO HAPPENED TO BE PASSING BY HAD HEARD EVERY WORD.

SHE TOLD THE QUEEN WHAT SHE HAD OVERHEARD—

I CAN'T BELIEVE IT!

YOU WILL, IF YOU VISIT THE MADHAVI BOWER THIS EVENING.

THAT EVENING AT THE MADHAVI BOWER—

SUSANGATA, YOU LOOK QUITE CHARMING DRESSED IN KANCHANA MALA'S CLOTHES AND SAGARIKA LOOKS JUST LIKE THE QUEEN. COME, THE KING IS WAITING.

WHEN VASANTAKA LED THEM TO UDAYANA—

MY DEAR SAGARIKA....

LOOK CAREFULLY, MY LORD! DOES EVERYONE LOOK LIKE SAGARIKA TO YOU?

YOU, VASAVADATTA!

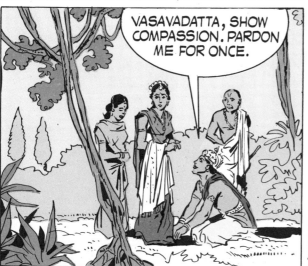

VASAVADATTA, SHOW COMPASSION. PARDON ME FOR ONCE.

WITHOUT SAYING ANOTHER WORD, VASAVADATTA WENT AWAY.

VASAVADATTA LOVES ME. SHE MUST BE HEART-BROKEN. SHE MAY EVEN KILL HERSELF....

MEANWHILE, SAGARIKA APPROACHED THE MADHAVI BOWER DRESSED IN THE QUEEN'S CLOTHES.

I SHOULDN'T HAVE AGREED TO COME HERE. IT IS IMPROPER.

LEAVE ME, MY LORD! LET ME DIE!

OH, IT'S SAGARIKA!

THROW AWAY THAT NOOSE FOR MY SAKE.

MY LORD!

MEANWHILE, THE QUEEN HAD DECIDED TO RETURN.

I SHOULD NOT HAVE BEEN CRUEL TO MY HUSBAND. HE WAS FULL OF REMORSE. I WILL GO BACK TO HIM.

BUT WHEN SHE REACHED THERE —

SAGARIKA AGAIN! MY LORD, IS THIS WORTHY OF YOU?

LET ME EXPLAIN, MY QUEEN. I MISTOOK HER FOR YOU.

AND I BROUGHT HIM HERE ONLY BECAUSE I THOUGHT IT WAS YOU.

AND HERE IS THE PROOF. LOOK AT THIS NOOSE!

KANCHANA MALA, BIND HIM WITH THIS VERY NOOSE...

... AND TAKE AWAY SAGARIKA AND LOCK HER UP.

HOW UNFORTUNATE I AM NOT TO HAVE BEEN ABLE TO DIE AS I WISHED!

AND KANCHANA MALA LED VASANTAKA AND SAGARIKA AWAY AS UDAYANA WATCHED HELPLESSLY.

BUT THE NEXT DAY THE QUEEN SET VASANTAKA FREE. SUSANGATA WENT TO MEET HIM.

SAGARIKA HAS SENT YOU THIS. YOU HAVE BEEN VERY SYMPATHETIC TO HER. PLEASE ACCEPT IT.

THE JEWEL-NECKLACE? THE SIGHT OF THIS MAY COMFORT MY FRIEND.

VASANTAKA TOOK THE NECKLACE TO KING UDAYANA—

VASANTAKA, YOU MUST PUT IT ON. LOOKING AT IT, I SHALL TRY TO TAKE COURAGE.

LATER IN THE AFTERNOON, A MAGICIAN FROM UJJAYINI CAME TO THE PALACE TO PERFORM BEFORE KING UDAYANA AND QUEEN VASAVADATTA.

HERE YOU SEE BRAHMA, VISHNU AND MAHESHWARA, AND THERE — THE APSARAS DANCING.

YOU FOOL, SHOW SAGARIKA IF YOU WANT TO PLEASE THE KING!

JUST THEN AN ATTENDANT CAME IN.

I BEG YOUR PARDON FOR INTERRUPTING, YOUR MAJESTY. BUT VASUBHUTI, THE MINISTER FROM SIMHALA, SEEKS AN AUDIENCE.

MY UNCLE'S MINISTER! WE SHOULD SEE HIM AT ONCE!

BUT, YOUR MAJESTY, YOU HAVEN'T SEEN MY BEST ITEM! PERMIT ME····

LATER, NOT NOW.

THEN VASUBHUTI ENTERED AND PAID HIS RESPECTS TO UDAYANA.

I BRING BAD NEWS: OUR SHIP HAS SUNK. ONLY YOUR ENVOY AND I MANAGED TO SURVIVE. YOUR BETROTHED, PRINCESS RATNAVALI, WHOM WE WERE BRINGING TO KAUSHAMBI WAS DROWNED IN THE STORMY SEA.

MY BETROTHED...

MY DEAR COUSIN! NO!!

JUST THEN—

FIRE! FIRE! THERE IS A FIRE IN THE INNER APARTMENT.

MY LORD! SAVE SAGARIKA! HER HANDS AND FEET HAVE BEEN BOUND ON MY ORDERS.

UDAYANA DASHED INTO THE INNER APARTMENTS.

SAGARIKA!

BUT...BUT...WHAT KIND OF FIRE IS THIS? NOT EVEN MY HAIR IS SINGED!

AND THE FIRE IS OUT!

MY FRIEND, THIS IS THE TRICK THE MAGICIAN WANTED YOU TO WITNESS — IT'S THE BEST PART OF HIS SHOW.

WHEN VASUBHUTI SAW SAGARIKA —

PRINCESS RATNAVALI!

OH! IS SHE RATNAVALI... MY COUSIN...?

MY LORD, I AM ASHAMED OF MYSELF. FREE HER OF THOSE BONDS.

I'LL DO AS YOU WISH, DEAR.

THEN VASUBHUTI EXPLAINED HOW RATNAVALI CAME TO BE BETROTHED TO KING UDAYANA ON THE INITIATIVE TAKEN BY YAUGANDHARAYANA.

MY LORD, I WONDER WHY YAUGANDHARAYANA TOLD US NOTHING.

HE MUST HAVE HAD HIS REASONS. WE'LL SEND FOR HIM.

YAUGANDHARAYANA CAME AT ONCE —

I HEARD A SAGE PROPHESY THAT THE MAN WHO MARRIES RATNAVALI WILL BECOME THE GREATEST OF KINGS . . .

. . . AND THAT'S WHY I TRIED TO BRING ABOUT A MARRIAGE BETWEEN YOU, MY LORD, AND THE PRINCESS OF SIMHALA.

THEN VASAVADATTA LED RATNAVALI TO UDAYANA.

MY LORD, ACCEPT MY COUSIN AS YOUR WIFE.

DIAL-A-COMIC

To buy any Amar Chitra Katha or Tinkle Comic

Call Toll Free on 1800-233-9125
(Mon-Fri 9.30 am to 6.00 pm IST
or leave a voice mail)

or

SMS 'ACK BUY' to 575758
and we will call you back

or

Log on to www.amarchitrakatha.com
to select your favourite comics and
read story-of-the-week online

TINKLE
WHERE LEARNING MEETS FUN

AMAR CHITRA KATHA